ECONOMICS OF GENETICALLY-MODIFIED WHEAT

COLIN A. CARTER
DEREK BERWALD
AL LOYNS

Canadian Cataloguing in Publication Data

Library and Archives Canada Cataloguing in Publication

Carter, Colin Andre
    The economics of genetically modified wheat / Colin A. Carter, Derek Berwald, Al Loyns.

(Monograph series on public policy and public administration ; 15)
Includes bibliographical references.
ISBN 0-7727-8617-8

1. Genetically modified foods—Economic aspects—Canada.
2. Wheat—Genetic engineering—Canada. 3. Wheat trade—Prairie Provinces.
4. Wheat trade—Canada. 5. Wheat—Canada—Marketing. I. Berwald, Derek, 1965- II. Loyns, Al, 1940- III. University of Toronto. Centre for Public Management IV. Title. V. Series.

HD9049.W5C2197 2005   338. 1'7311'09712   C2005-905830-7

Printed for the University of Toronto Centre for Public Management by University of Toronto Press.

ACKNOWLEDGEMENTS

We thank the following individuals for their helpful comments and suggestions on earlier drafts of this book: Nicholas Kalaitzandonakes, Kurt Klein, Peter Phillips, Carman Read, Curtis Rempel, Andrew Stark, Anthony Temple, and Bill Wilson. In addition, many individuals in Canada, the US, Asia, and Europe provided valuable information and data. This research was partially funded by Monsanto Canada.

TABLE OF CONTENTS

PREFACE

In *The Economics of Genetically Modified Wheat*, Colin Carter, Derek Berwald, and Al Loyns offer a troubling prognosis for Canada's wheat industry but also a promising prescription: the introduction of genetically-modified wheat.

A crop becomes genetically modified when genes from another organism are introduced into it, with the aim of making it more resistant to herbicides, pests, or disease, thus lowering input costs and increasing yield per acre.

But as with many innovations, the acceptance of genetically-modified wheat will require a gestalt shift on the part of those whose political ideologies, regulatory structures and business models would have to change as a result. These include environmentalists who fear the consequences of tinkering with natural processes, the Canadian Wheat Board, which is concerned with the possible loss of markets and the technological issues involved in segregating genetically-modified from non-modified wheat, and much of the Canadian food processing industry, worried as it is about boycotts by environmentalists. As a result, genetically-modified wheat is not grown in Canada. But, increasingly, it will be elsewhere, thus threatening Canada's market share.

The Economics of Genetically Modified Wheat is an attempt to encourage a shift in worldview: to address these concerns and show that genetically-modified wheat is a viable option for North American wheat farmers. As far as environmental issues are concerned, the authors note that one of genetically-modified wheat's main impacts is to reduce the use of herbicide by commercial farmers, with environmentally-friendly consequences.

As for the economic concerns that genetically-modified wheat raises, growth in world demand for wheat will come more and more from developing countries, which are by and large interested only in cheap wheat. Countries such as China, Indonesia and Mexico, the authors argue, will thus become increasingly open to the genetically modified variant. And while the Canadian Wheat Board believes that it would be prohibitively costly to segregate genetically-modified from non-modified wheat, the authors' research disputes this claim.

All in all, Carter, Berwald and Loyns estimate that for Canadian wheat farmers, the present value of introducing genetically-modified wheat would be $3.6 billion. "The benefits of growing GM wheat are so great," they conclude, that introducing it "into Canada is the correct decision now."

The Economics of Genetically Modified Wheat is the fifteenth monograph in the University of Toronto Centre for Public Management Monograph Series, which is funded by a generous grant from the Donner Canadian Foundation. The authors' own research was supported, in part, by a grant from Monsanto Canada.

Andrew Stark
Editor
University of Toronto Centre for
Public Management Monograph Series

SUMMARY

The cost-benefit analysis for Round-Up Ready wheat was clearly negative, and that is why there was so much agreement among farmers that it was the wrong product at the wrong time.
                    Canadian Wheat Board, "Grain Matters" July/Aug 2004.

This statement from the Canadian Wheat Board (CWB) reads as if it is the only and final evidence required to assess the economics of Genetically Modified (GM) wheat in Canada. In fact, the cost-benefit analysis of GM wheat to which the CWB refers in the above statement cannot be replicated, and we believe that its reported conclusions were wrong. The Board sponsored an economics study at the University of Saskatchewan on this question and when we attempted to duplicate those results, we found the benefits exceed the costs for GM wheat on the Canadian prairies. So the Board's own research does not even back up the claim that genetically modified wheat is "the wrong product at the wrong time."

The entire *Grain Matters* statement is false because most farmers would have little idea as to what cost-benefit analysis really provides. It is more probable that wheat farmers make up their minds on evidence and perceptions other than one economic approach to investment decision making. The above statement is another example of the CWB distorting the facts to make its case on an issue, under the guise of representing wheat producers.

Furthermore, it is completely misleading for the Board to claim that there was widespread agreement among prairie farmers on this issue. GM canola in several forms has been adopted widely across the prairies because it has many desirable attributes and few negatives. Both GM and Non-GM soybeans are successfully grown in Canada and segregated in the marketing chain without problems. There are many commercial farmers who have indicated that they would experiment with GM wheat in the same manner in which they experimented with GM canola and soybeans when these crops were first introduced. However, as in many other cases of the introduction of technological advance in the prairie grain industry, the regulators intervened and prevailed, on the basis of limited and incomplete research. This book documents, as no other analysis has done so far, how this example of regulatory inflexibility terminated what may have been a positive step forward in wheat technology on the prairies. In this book we apply economic analysis to several dimensions of measuring the economic impacts of GM wheat. We find that this new technology could have very favorable implications for producers, the prairie economy, and for Canada as a whole. In other words, it may well be "the right product at the right time."

Wheat is a struggling industry in western Canada and growers are shifting away from wheat due to its low profitability and its over-regulation. Canada's relative importance in the global wheat market has fallen. Alternatively, canola acreage has expanded significantly in western Canada and growth of export sales has been strong. The commercialization of genetically modified canola has been a huge success story on the Canadian prairies, and has had a positive environmental impact (Brimner, Gallivan, and Stephenson). As a result, Canada is recognized as one of the leading adopters of crop biotechnology in the world.

Genetically modified (GM) wheat offers some potential to turn around the wheat industry on the Canadian prairies. Rather than exploring ways that this new technology could be used to improve grower returns, the Canadian Wheat Board (CWB) and others categorically rejected the introduction of Roundup Ready® or other GM wheat in Canada, due to a fear of lost markets. The CWB threatened to sue Monsanto if Roundup Ready® wheat passed the crop varietal registration process in Canada, which it probably would have. However, Monsanto withdrew from its GM wheat program in North America in May 2004, largely in response to political pressure from the CWB (F.O. Licht, May 2004).

This monograph is an economic assessment of the potential economic value of GM wheat to the prairie grain industry. Most of the research reported here was conducted prior to the May 2004 announcement that Monsanto was pulling out of GM wheat. However, in some ways the May 2004 announcement by Monsanto elevates the importance of the information in this study. The important policy counterfactual ("but for") question is: *what would the economic impact have been in the absence of the Monsanto decision to withdraw from GM wheat?* Other companies (e.g., Syngenta) besides Monsanto are pursuing similar technology, so this is not necessarily the end of GM wheat for Canada.

GM Wheat Adoption in Canada
The opposition to the introduction of GM wheat in Canada, led by the CWB and others, is based on concerns over loss of markets and negative agronomic impacts, such as the cost of controlling volunteer wheat that is resistant to Roundup. Most of the Canadian food processing industry is also opposed to GM wheat. These firms don't see GM wheat's intro-

duction leading to a significant boost in their profits because wheat is typically a small share of input costs for most processed food products. The food processors are afraid of losing market share if environmental activist groups decide to stage a boycott of food products containing GM wheat. The success of any such boycott is doubtful because a very large percentage of processed foods sold in Canada today contain some GM ingredients. Compared to the EU, consumers in Canada have trust in the food safety regulatory process.

Markets for Canadian HRS Wheat

Despite claims by the CWB and several economists a decade ago that important wheat import markets were highly dependent on Canadian wheat, and could not possibly substitute away from Canadian western red spring (CWRS), Canada's market share has fallen dramatically in some key markets. This is clear evidence that the global wheat market is increasingly competitive. Future growth in import demand will originate in developing countries that are unwilling to pay premiums for relatively high quality wheat. Yet the CWB continues to promote the idea that a large share of the world market is willing to pay price premiums for high quality Canadian wheat. The facts are that western Canada competes mainly in lower quality wheat markets (e.g., the Philippines and Indonesia) that are price sensitive and substitution among wheat grades and classes is high.

The CWB maintains that "82 percent of Canadian farmers' markets for Canadian Western Red Spring wheat indicate they would not or could not buy GM wheat." We estimate that approximately 80% of the market for Canadian spring wheat will accept GM wheat, after an initial transition period. Most of the large world wheat importers (e.g., Brazil, Egypt, Iran, China, Indonesia, Mexico, and the Philippines) are interested in low priced wheat and they will not pay a price premium for non-GM wheat.

Along with the EU, Japan has voiced strong opposition to GM wheat, even though there is a considerable amount of GM food eaten in Japan today. Roundup Ready® wheat would contain exactly the same herbicide tolerant gene that has been inserted into Roundup Ready® canola, which has been accepted in all major markets around the world, including Japan. If their opposition to GM wheat is genuine, this is not a problem as Japan would simply pay a small price premium for non-GM wheat, as they do in the soybean and corn markets now. About 25% of the corn and 20% of the soybean imports into Japan are non-GM under a cost-effective segregation system with a 5% tolerance level. The marketplace would soon develop a similar system for non-GM wheat.

The EU is one of Canada's major competitors in world wheat markets. With its generous farm subsidies, the EU can well afford to oppose GM wheat, but the same is not the case for Canadian prairie farmers.

Segregation of non-GM from GM wheat
The commercialization of GM wheat on the Canadian prairies is conditional upon the implementation of an effective segregation or identity preservation (IP) system. The CWB has suggested that the cost to segregate GM and non-GM wheat would be prohibitive given the current grain-handling system. The Canadian Grain Commission's Variety Eligibility Declaration (VED) proposal would have contributed directly to any segregation system for non-GM wheat but this was opposed by the industry, highlighting the fact that the Canadian grain handling system is out of sync with other parts of the developed world when it comes to sourcing grain by variety.

In fact, there is a wide variety of segregation and IP programs in the prairie grain industry today. For instance a large bakery in the U.K. has set up a very successful identity preservation type system to procure three wheat varieties from the Canadian prairies specific to the bakery's needs. We provide cost estimates of segregating non-GM wheat in the Canadian bulk handling system, with GM wheat exceeding fifty percent of total wheat acreage on the prairies. We assume the segregation system will involve wheat being assembled, handled and transported through the bulk handling system in a "sequenced" manner similar to the present practice of "runs" of grain through high throughput facilities. The cost of segregation in Canada under this type of system would be approximately 7 to 11¢ per bushel.

Due to segregation requirements and the higher unit cost production of non-GM wheat, this introduces the potential for a price premium for non-GM wheat. As a result, non-adopters of GM wheat on the Canadian prairies may indirectly benefit from the introduction of GM wheat.

GM Wheat's Potential Economic Value to Growers and the Industry
A Grain Industry Working Group on GM Wheat was established in 2001, and this group came up with several necessary conditions for the commercialization of GM wheat in Canada. The Group endorsed the *real options* approach for evaluating the economic merits of GM wheat introduction. Following their suggestion, we use the real options approach in this report, which accounts for the effects of uncertainty surrounding the decision to adopt GM wheat and quantifies the value of waiting to adopt.

GENETICALLY MODIFIED WHEAT

Using field trial data and market and cost of production information, we first measure the impact on financial returns to the typical prairie farmer from adopting GM wheat compared to conventional wheat varieties, under a standard crop rotation. The estimated gains associated with adopting GM wheat have a range, but our point estimates are from $9 to over $18 per acre, depending on the soil zone. With multiple years and rotation considerations, the benefits are slightly lower due to costs of controlling volunteer GM wheat. Our baseline assumption is a technology fee of $7 per acre and a 9% yield increase from GM wheat. Sensitivity analysis is performed, allowing these baseline assumptions to vary.

Our real options estimates suggest that after accounting for the market impacts and segregation costs, the immediate adoption of GM wheat is optimal for Canada. The benefit-cost ratio is over 4.5, far above the real options threshold ratio. As the adoption percentage increases, the benefit-cost ratio increases. The estimated annual net benefits to all Canadian wheat growers are about $287 million per year, with a present value of $3.6 billion.

The CWB's political influence has resulted in Monsanto halting development of GM wheat technology in both Canada and the United States. Now that GM wheat has been rejected in North America, we ask the question: What if third country competitors in the world market adopt GM wheat? We find that Canadian wheat farmers would lose about $100 million per year.

Conclusion

This monograph demonstrates that western Canadian farmers will lose international competitiveness now that the commercialization of GM wheat has been rejected in Canada. The blanket opposition to GM wheat by the CWB, farm groups, and other organizations ignores the reality that this technology may soon be adopted in other parts of the world. This may be yet another example of where regulation has held back the prairie grain industry and cost it money.

The results of our research are that the benefits to adoption of GM wheat are so great that introducing GM wheat into Canada is the correct decision now. The benefits of growing GM wheat at the farm level are significant enough that, after a transition period, GM wheat would be adopted widely on prairie acreage.

1. OVERVIEW OF THE ISSUES SURROUNDING THE COMMERCIALIZATION OF GM WHEAT IN CANADA

The campaign of fear now being waged against genetic modification is based largely on fantasy and a complete lack of respect for science and logic. Genetic modification can reduce the chemical load in the environment, and reduce the amount of land required for food crops.
Dr. Patrick Moore, ecologist and co-founder of Greenpeace, March 2001.

For his support of bioengineered crops, involving the transfer of genes between plants, the main environmental activist groups (including his own Greenpeace) have accused Patrick Moore of being a turncoat. His dispute with his fellow environmentalists underscores the controversy surrounding the commercial production and marketing of genetically modified (GM) foods. This global controversy recently focused on GM spring wheat, as Monsanto had applied for food, feed, and environmental safety approval of GM Roundup Ready® wheat in Canada, the US, and Japan.[1] The purpose of this book is to evaluate whether or not the Canadian wheat industry would benefit from the adoption and commercialization of GM wheat, under current market and policy conditions in Canada and elsewhere. If they start to grow GM wheat, farmers on the prairies will want to know if it can be sold, how it will affect the bottom line returns per acre, if they can control the volunteer GM wheat in subsequent years, and whether it reduces or increases crop management costs. This introductory and overview chapter summarizes what we know about the main issues associated with adopting GM wheat in Canada. We try to explain why there is some opposition to GM wheat in Canada, and we report our key research findings. Additional research details are provided in the subsequent chapters.

The genetic modification of plants has gone on for thousands of years (Paarlberg, 2000). Over the last few hundred years, scientific varietal selection and crossing of wheat has genetically modified it numerous times. Transgenic crops, like Roundup Ready® wheat, are developed by transferring genes from one organism to another. For instance, the Roundup tolerant gene comes from a natural bacterium, which is found in the soil. Adding DNA to the wheat genome in a laboratory initially produces transgenic wheat lines, but the plant can later pass on that DNA through normal processes.

Compared to traditional plant breeding, biotechnology can produce new varieties of plants more quickly and efficiently. In addition, biotechnology can introduce desirable traits into plants that could not be established through conventional breeding techniques. In many countries around the world, research is ongoing that will introduce genes into wheat that will give the plant resistance to herbicides, insects, disease, drought and salts in the soil. Ongoing GM wheat research programs are also aimed at improving flour quality.

Compared to conventional crops, the potential benefits of transgenic plants to farmers and the environment are quite straightforward. Farmers may stand to gain due to better weed and pest control, less tillage, improved crop quality, and higher yields. In addition, the new bioengineered crops may require fewer chemicals and therefore may be more environmentally friendly. This technology offers lower farm production costs, increased farm profits, and a more efficient industry.

In the past seven years, worldwide growth in GM crop acres has been double-digit and totals about 170 million acres as of 2003. Despite the controversy surrounding biotechnology, the rapid adoption of biotech crops is virtually unprecedented in the history of agriculture. Table 1.1 shows adoption rates in North America. More than 20% of global soybeans, corn, cotton and canola acres are now planted to biotech varieties. Biotech soybeans were first grown in 1996 and by 2003 they accounted for 55% of the world's soybean acreage. The US, Argentina, Canada,

Table 1.1. Percent of Acres Planted to Herbicide-Tolerant (HT) and Bt Crop Varieties, North America, 1996-2003

	1996	1997	1998	1999	2000	2001	2002	2003
				%				
US								
Corn:								
Bt & HT	4	11	28	33	25	26	34	40
Soybeans:								
HT	7.4	17	44.2	55.8	54	68	75	81
Cotton:								
Bt & HT	17	25	43	74	61	68	71	73
Canada								
HT Canola	2	17	40	54	55	58	65	73

Note: Data for corn and cotton includes Bt and HT traits, and stacked varieties–containing both Bt and HT tolerant genes. An estimated 25% of the cotton acreage may be stacked traits, while for corn it around 4%. Source: USDA, NASS for US data and Angus Reid Market Watch for Canada.

Brazil, China, and South Africa are leading growers of biotech crops, mostly herbicide tolerant (73%) and insect resistant (18%) crops. Bt crop varieties have genes that give them resistance to particular insects, while HT crops have genes that give them resistance to specific herbicides, such as glyphosate (known as Roundup). A small percentage (8%) of the biotech world acreage is crops with stacked traits–both herbicide tolerant and insect resistant.[2]

In addition to biotech crops, biotech ingredients and biotech processes are used in the production of a wide selection of food and beverage products such as poultry, dairy products, and beer. For example, most cheese is made with genetically engineered enzymes. Furthermore, GM-based pharmaceuticals for humans are very common today. Vaccines and insulin are produced by genetically modifying organisms, as are many other drugs. Scientists have also started engineering plants to produce a wide variety of pharmaceuticals, and if successful this will lead to more affordable drugs.

As much as 70% of the processed foods sold in Canada could contain some GM ingredients (Phillips and Corkindale). There are also plenty of GM foods eaten in the European Union (EU) and Japan. Roundup Ready® wheat would contain exactly the same herbicide tolerant gene that has been inserted into Roundup Ready® canola, which has been accepted in all major markets around the world. So why has the commercialization of GM wheat become such a big political issue? We try to address this question below.[3]

GM Wheat Adoption in Canada
The Canadian Wheat Board (CWB) is strongly opposed to the introduction of Roundup Ready® wheat in Canada and its opposition is apparently based on concerns over loss of markets and negative agronomic impacts, such as the cost of controlling volunteer Roundup Ready® wheat.[4] However, the CWB has not provided any compelling evidence supporting their claims. In 2001 an Industry Working Group on GM Wheat (made up of farmers, industry and government representatives) was established to define a comprehensive set of conditions that should be met before any GM wheat variety could be marketed in Canada. In February 2003, the Working Group identified the following conditions necessary for the adoption of GM wheat in Canada:

- Market acceptance: Markets for the entire GM wheat crop would have to be identified, and the ability to meet the demand for non-GM wheat would have to be demonstrated;

- Segregation system: An accurate, quick, and inexpensive technology is needed to detect the presence of GM wheat, from the primary elevator right through the entire system.
- Agronomics: A clear understanding of the impact of GM wheat adoption on farm management practices and profitability with respect to each type of farming operation (e.g., conventional tillage, conservation tillage, organic, pesticide-free, etc.), across a multi-year rotation.
- Cost-benefit analysis: A cost-benefit analysis is needed that measures agronomic impacts (i.e., yield and cost effects), market impacts, and segregation costs. The Working Group recommended using the real options value approach, employed by University of Saskatchewan economists to estimate the economic impacts of GM wheat adoption.[5]

We agree with much of the Working Group's report and we believe that stakeholders in the Canadian wheat industry are concerned with the following issues surrounding the commercialization of GM wheat:

2. **Environmental** concerns such as pollen flow, volunteer biotech wheat, and unwanted cross-pollination;
3. **Market demand** concerns, as there is some fear of losing key international markets, because certain buyers may refuse to purchase GM wheat;
4. For those customers who do not want GM wheat, there are **segregation and identity preservation** concerns.[6] Many foreign countries have mandatory GM labeling regulations, which would establish threshold levels for adventitious presence of GM material in non-GM wheat; and
5. Overall **economic impact on farmers** from adopting GM wheat and associated impact on non-adopters.

In addition to the working group's recommendations, the CWB called for a benefit-cost analysis of GM wheat that accounts for market impact and overall farmer revenue.[7] The CWB suggested that the benefit-cost study be part of the registration process. It must be noted that market analysis has never been applied as a criterion in crop varietal registration in Canadian agriculture. The Board is therefore proposing a major change to the crop varietal registration process in Canada, and their proposal was rejected by the Canadian Food Inspection Agency (CFIA), the government agency responsible for these matters. In this report, we provide a benefit cost analysis of the type called for by the CWB. As part of our analysis, we address the above four issues identified by the working group, and we focus on those points that require economics analysis.

Environmental Concerns

This book does not devote much space to the environmental issues surrounding biotech wheat. There are at least three reasons for this decision. **First**, many of the environmental questions cannot be addressed with economics because they involve ecological and plant biology issues. However, economics can assess the benefits and costs of environmental issues and the option value approach that we use below (in Chapter 4) is useful in this regard. **Second**, GM wheat poses fewer environmental issues compared to some of the other GM crops such as soybeans or cotton. As explained by Glover:

> *Wheat is primarily self-pollinating, producing small amounts of pollen that has a short viability period. Potential gene flow is minimal at distances greater than 1 m from the source plant and this is reflected by the absence of any separation distances required between wheat crops for certified seed production.* (J. Glover, p.viii).

Third, the Canadian government's licensing process for any new GM crop variety carefully evaluates the quality of the proposed variety, and assesses any risks the new variety may present for the environment and human health. We have no reason to question this scientific process. The Canadian Food Inspection Agency (CFIA) is responsible for the environmental assessment, and Health Canada is responsible for ensuring that GM foods are safe for human consumption, either directly or indirectly. The main GM wheat opponent, the CWB, has not challenged this biosafety approval process, except to argue that it should include a benefit-cost analysis.[8]

Part of the review process in the Canadian regulatory procedure consists of examining the issue of whether volunteer GM wheat could become a problem weed, or the possible transfer of herbicide resistance to other weeds. This is also an issue for herbicide tolerant canola and it requires effective crop management to minimize problems. However, this concern is not confined to GM crops as non-GM herbicide tolerant crops are available in Canada (e.g., Clearfield wheat). As of crop year 2005-06, western Canadian wheat growers will have access to herbicide tolerant Clearfield wheat. Furthermore, common weeds also build up herbicide resistance over time and this has become a major problem in Canada and elsewhere. For example, California (non-GM) rice production is experiencing what has been called an "epidemic" of herbicide resistance in weeds. In North America, herbicide resistant weeds in non-GM spring wheat are also a significant and growing problem (Gianessi et al.), and its relevance to GM wheat is the issue of developing counter measures.

GM technology is perhaps more environmentally friendly than other farming methods. In an interesting article, Jonathan Rauch argues that genetic modification of crops may be the most environmentally beneficial technology that has emerged in decades, or perhaps centuries. He explains why farming non-GM crops are putting pressure on the environment. Rauch also compares biotech crop practices with other methods of farming and makes the following points:

• Organic farming uses no artificial fertilizer, but it does use manure, which can pollute water and contaminate food;
• Compared to commercial agriculture, traditional farmers may use less herbicide, but they also do more ploughing, with environmental complications; and
• Compared to commercial agriculture, low-input agriculture uses fewer chemicals but more land.

The potential environmental benefits of GM crops have already been observed for Canadian canola. The share of the total canola acreage that is genetically modified in Canada increased from 10% to 80% since the late 1990s. This caused herbicide use to decrease by 40%, and an index of the environmental impact measuring environmental persistence, human, and animal toxicity to fall by 36% over the same time frame (Brimner, Gallivan and Stephenson).

In Chapter 4 we do account for potential environmental costs, although we believe these costs are rather small. On a net basis, GM wheat may indeed provide environmental benefits.

Market Demand Concerns
Roundup Ready® wheat is classified as a "first generation" type bio-engineered plant, created to reduce the use of chemical inputs (Nelson). Second generation biotech wheat varieties will offer superior baking qualities and improved dietary and nutritional advantages. Despite the global success of biotech crops generally, the planned commercialization of first-generation biotech wheat in North America has met with both domestic and foreign opposition. What gives rise to this opposition and why is GM wheat being treated so differently than existing GM crops?

Compared to GM crops that have approval, we believe the main difference with wheat is that it is a major food grain, whereas GM corn and soybeans are major feed grains. Furthermore, canola is a relatively minor crop in the world food equation. GM canola is used primarily for food but canola oil (and soybean and corn oil) are exempt from labeling regulations in Japan and elsewhere, and so has not met with much consumer resistance. The EU and Japan now have strict mandatory GM food labeling laws but the impact of these regulations on canola, corn, and soybeans has been relatively small, compared to the possible effect on wheat if it is commercialized. However, the situation is changing in the EU and this may raise issues with GM vegetable oils. As of 2004, the new food biotech labeling regulations in the EU require the labeling of food products containing canola, corn and soybean oil, even though the genetically modified DNA may not be detectable in some of these food products. During the processing of these oils the GM DNA (and the associated protein) is denatured. In theory, the refined oils do not contain any DNA and so it cannot be determined through DNA testing whether or not the oil was produced from GM seeds. In contrast, flour produced from GM wheat will have DNA that can be easily detected.

Wheat is actually the world's major food crop and about 75 percent of the world's wheat production is consumed as food. In comparison, only 20% of the annual corn and soybean supply is consumed directly as food. Given the importance of wheat as a food grain, GM wheat has become a target of those (mainly western Europeans and environmental activists) who are opposed to GM technology. Alternatively, because of its importance as a food, we believe that biotech wheat offers tremendous potential for modern agriculture. For instance, wheat could be the first biotech food crop to offer significant benefits to developing countries.

Wheat can be grown in a wide range of environments, and so world production is more geographically diversified compared to corn, canola and soybeans. In addition, compared to the other major grains and oilseeds, wheat is unique in that it can be used to produce a variety of food products including raised bread, flat bread, pasta, cakes and noodles.

In Canada, the market concerns over GM wheat arise primarily from the CWB's opposition to GM wheat, and this position receives support from the domestic Canadian flour millers, environmental groups such as Greenpeace, and some farm groups.[9] Two CWB representatives have explained:

> *...82% of Canadian farmers' markets for Canadian western red spring wheat still indicate that they would not, or could not, buy GM wheat.*
> Ken Ritter, chairman of the CWB, testimony to Standing Committee on Agriculture and Agri-Food, 37th Parliament, 2nd Session, April 3, 2003.

I think it's clear that a cost-benefit analysis on Roundup Ready wheat would indicate a net loss for farmers. In fact there is University of Saskatchewan research that indicates that both users of the technology and non-adopters would face negative returns while the technology developer would have positive returns.

Bill Nicholson, CWB Director, *ibid.*

...the unconfined release of Roundup Ready wheat could very well spell disaster for the Canadian and American wheat industries when buyers around the world have said they don't want it.

Adrian Measner, President and CEO of the CWB, speech given to the National Grain Trade Council, September 18, 2003.

There are at least four main reasons for the opposition to GM wheat from the CWB and others, with backing from Canadian food processors:

1. The CWB does not wish to jeopardize key markets for high quality spring wheat in Japan and the U.K., where some consumers perceive GM crops as having a negative impact on the environment, and possibly being unsafe to eat.
2. The CWB is worried about accidental GM contamination of non-GM wheat shipments to Japan and the UK, and the CWB suggests it is impossible to segregate non-GM from GM wheat to meet established tolerance levels;
3. Economics research at the University of Saskatchewan suggests that prairie farmers will be worse off with the commercialization of GM wheat; and
4. Canadian food processors see nothing in this new technology for them, because wheat is typically a small input cost share of most processed food products. So even if first-generation GM wheat leads to a larger wheat crop and slightly lower wheat prices, the food processors will realize little profit gain. These processors spend considerable sums of money advertising national labels and do not want to risk losing any market share as a result of any potential anti-GM boycott by environmental groups. At the same time, they do not want to pay a higher price for non-GM wheat.

The CWB staunchly maintains that customers and prairie farmers do not want GM wheat. According to this government organization, about 80% of its customers would reject GM wheat and would take their business elsewhere if Canada commercializes GM wheat. So the demand side of the equation is crucial. We arrive at a much different conclusions from the

CWB's declaration on market share impacts. We find that initially non-GM wheat would sell at approximately a 5 to 10% (fob) price premium over GM wheat and at most 15 to 20% of the CWB's sales would be non-GM, much lower than the CWB's predicted market share for non-GM wheat.

Furtan, Gray and Holzman (2003b) provide an estimate of the potential market for non-GM wheat and they include Iran and Brazil in their list of countries that would not import GM wheat (see their footnote 16). We have interviewed experts in the grain trade and there is absolutely no evidence to suggest that Iran would pay a premium for non-GM wheat. Iran has no regulations on GM food labeling and a considerable amount of processed food containing GM material now enters that country. We are not aware of any consumer opposition to GM food in Iran. Furthermore, Iran has become a much less important market for the CWB in the last few years.

Furtan, Gray and Holzman (2003b) find that about 35% of the CWB's overseas customers for spring wheat would not import GM varieties. This amounts to about 25% of total CWB spring wheat sales. Iran has accounted for about 10% of CWB annual sales. So if we net out Iran from Furtan Gray and Holzman's calculation, our estimate of 20% of the market rejecting GM wheat is very similar to theirs.

Most of the large world wheat importers (e.g., Brazil, Egypt, Iran, Indonesia, Mexico, and the Philippines) are interested in low priced wheat and they would not pay a price premium for non-GM wheat. Our estimate of the 5 to 10% price premium for non-GM wheat is based largely on the evidence that price premia exist for non-GM corn in Japan and South Korea, non-GM soybeans in Japan, and non-GM corn in the US, typically ranging from 3 to 8 percent (Foster, Berry and Hogan).

The EU, as a major player in world food markets, exerts regulatory influence over many other countries (Paarlberg, 2002). The strict European regulations are serving to delay the introduction of GM crops in many countries. For example, largely because of the EU's staunch opposition to transgenic crops, commercial release of the famous "golden rice" is on hold. This rice variety has the potential to reduce vitamin A deficiency in developing countries, alleviating malnutrition and blindness. But this GM technology does little for French consumers and so they are opposed. Rich countries with highly subsidized agriculture like France can afford to shun new agricultural technology, but poor countries like those in Asia and Africa cannot. We are not even sure that prairie wheat farmers can afford to forgo this improved technology.

GM food policies in large countries such as Japan, China and Russia are partly controlled by a spillover from fears in the EU over potential risks to human health and the environment. What happens in the EU may be important regarding Japan or China's view on GM wheat. Zambia's refusal of GM corn as food aid in the face of massive starvation in the fall of 2002 caught the world's attention and underscored the influence of the EU on this matter.

We note that the main opposition to GM crops in the EU is due to concerns over potential environmental impacts. In other words, any potential human health risk associated with GM crops is becoming a non-issue. The environmental activist groups (e.g., Greenpeace and Friends of the Earth) have rallied around the environmental fears as part of their anti-globalization movement. These groups argue that GM crops could cross with related species and disrupt the ecosystem. This is a politically appealing argument in the EU. Large shares of European consumers simply do not trust their own regulatory process when it comes to food and agriculture. Such fear is no doubt related to the way the European governments have handled food scares such as the BSE outbreak, that have no relationship to GM crops.

With the release of more scientific tests and improved knowledge of GM crops among the general public, opposition to GM foods in the EU is declining. EU consumers are now more accepting of GM because the World Health Organization (WHO) and several national scientific academies in Europe and around the world have judged biotech foods to be as safe as conventional non-GM foods.[10]

In the United Kingdom, a recent review of scientific findings concluded there is no evidence to suggest that GM crops are less safe to eat than conventional foods (UK GM Science Review Panel). This conclusion echoes that of the 2002 report by the Canadian Biotechnology Advisory Committee. In 2004, Britain approved the planting of herbicide tolerant GM corn, and this decision sends a strong signal that biotech crops are not dead in the EU.

While it is true that consumer attitudes in certain European countries may be shifting in favor of greater tolerance of GM foods, there remains variation in attitude across member countries. A March 2003 Eurobarometer[11] EU study on consumer attitudes in the EU reported that:

[a]fter a decade of continually declining optimism in biotechnology the trend reverses in 2002.

The British Food Standards Agency is an independent food safety watch-dog set up by an Act of Parliament in 2000 to protect the British public's health and consumer interests in relation to food. The Food Standards Agency's most recent survey[12] found a significant decrease in concern about GM foods–from 43% in 2000 to 38% in 2003.

Another European wide study by KRC research[13] concluded that con-sumer views towards agricultural biotechnology have become less nega-tive. The report found that:

> ...consumers across Europe are less likely than before to say genetically modified crops and foods will upset the balance of nature and pose risks to the environment. This suggests that, as consumers continue to get more balanced information on biotechnology, concerns about environmental impacts could decrease further.

In a French study of consumer attitudes towards GM food, Noussair, Robin and Ruffieux concluded that the anti-GMO sentiment typically found in consumer surveys may not be reflected in actual purchase behavior. Using experimental economics, Noussair, Robin, and Ruffieux found that about two-thirds of French consumers would be willing to purchase a GM food product if it was priced right. They argued that the segregation of the mar-ket into GM and non-GM food products would create economic value. At the same time, French farmers are also calling for authorization to grow GM corn varieties to allow them to fight against pest problems.

The Regulatory Framework
The CWB is a statutory marketing agency and is controlled by the feder-al government. As stated by Morris Rosenberg, the Deputy Attorney General of Canada:

> Under the Canadian Wheat Board Act, the Board was not and is not accountable directly to individual producers. Rather, the Board was and is accountable to Parliament.
> Notice of Motion, Federal Court of Canada-Trial Division,
> Court File No. T-215-02, June 17, 2003.

This organization is driven by bureaucratic decision making, which means that innovation and change are typically met with resistance within this agency (Loyns and Carter; Canada Grains Council (1989); Carter, Loyns, and Berwald). The licensing of semi-dwarf wheat varieties was vigorously resisted by the CWB in the 1980s, and this cost prairie farmers hundreds of millions of dollars (Carter, Loyns and Ahmadi-Esfahani; Henning and Martin). Protein segregation was initially resisted by the CWB. Long standing CWB opposition to competition among companies that handle CWB grains is another example that has cost farmers (Parsons and Wilson). So it is no surprise that the CWB is opposed to GM wheat. Their response is rational bureaucratic behavior, which may or may not be in the best interests of the prairie wheat farmers. GM wheat is new technology with uncertain impacts and there is no good bureaucratic reason to support its commercialization. This new crop would serve to increase the workload of CWB marketers. Opposition to GM wheat in Japan and the United Kingdom (two remaining high quality markets) also has an undue influence on the CWB's position regarding this new technology. These two markets combined account for about 12% of the CWB's annual wheat sales.

Carter, Loyns and Berwald (1998) provided detailed estimates of the domestic inefficiencies generated by the CWB.[14] They found that some of the excessive costs generated by the CWB fit the bureaucratic decision making framework very closely (e.g., excessive handling and cleaning and overage credits).

A 1995 KPMG report on grain logistics found the Canadian logistical system is plagued with inefficiencies due to such factors as lack of economic incentives, lack of accountability, excess segregation, and excess cleaning. They estimated that up to 20% of operational costs could be saved annually through reduced regulation, the introduction of transparent incentives, and improved accountability. The KPMG study was financed by western Canada's eight major grain companies, the two railways, and the three major public agencies (i.e., the Grain Transportation Agency, the Canadian Grain Commission, and the CWB). Its objective was to look for ways to improve the operating efficiency of Canada's grain logistics system.

The Canadian federal government remains unwilling to reduce the regulatory powers of the CWB, including the controversial role that the CWB plays in grain transportation. In an exhaustive 1998 report on the transportation question, Justice Willard Estey reached the conclusion that control over grain handling and transportation is not a proper role for the CWB. Estey wrote:

Apart from sales and marketing, it is recommended that the Board have no operational or commercial role in the handling and transportation of grain.

The story of the Estey report and the Canadian federal government's non-response to Estey's recommendations provides insights about the current political influence enjoyed by the CWB. The CWB and its single desk supporters were quick to criticize Justice Estey and accused him of being biased because in his report he questioned the economic benefits of the central planning role of the CWB.

Estey made a number of recommendations (on grain cleaning, branch line abandonment, fuel tax and road transportation, etc.) but the significant findings dealt with the role of the CWB in planning prairie grain shipments and the overall lack of commercial accountability throughout the western Canadian grain handling system. Estey found that the bureaucratic system of rail car allocation was costing farmers money and he made the strong recommendation that the CWB should become a buyer of grain at the export port, not at the farm and country elevator. Estey argued that competition in rail transportation, rather than regulation, would best serve the interests of farmers. Estey did not provide any new empirical evidence on the inefficiencies associated with the CWB's control of the grain handling and transportation system. However, he was clearly influenced by the numerous studies that have carefully documented the cost to Canadian farmers of over-regulation in grain handling and transportation.

Initially the federal government appeared to endorse the Estey report and the government appointed Arthur Kroeger to work with various stakeholder groups to implement Estey's proposals to deregulate grain transportation. However, this effort largely failed, as Kroeger was unable to obtain consensus from the stakeholders and the federal government backed away from the strongest of the Estey recommendations. Instead, in the spring of 2000, the federal government expanded the CWB's regulatory authority over grain handling and transportation and further entrenched the centralized role of the CWB in grain transportation.

This federal government decision to sweep the Estey report under the rug is indicative of the political strength of the CWB. The continuation of the CWB's control over domestic grain handling and transportation is politically significant because it indicates that the federal government continues to support the regulatory powers of the CWB despite strong evidence of inefficiencies that result from the lack of a commercial system.

Prior to the Estey report, the Canadian Minister of Agriculture and Agri-Food, had appointed a Western Grain Marketing Panel (WGMP) to examine prairie grain marketing issues. After extensive discussions and hearings with all players in the industry, the WGMP report was released in July, 1996. The key recommendations of the WGMP were as follows:

- Remove the CWB monopoly on feed barley for export markets;
- Remove the CWB's marketing authority over organic wheat and unlicensed wheat;
- Provide farmers with the option of marketing a portion of their CWRS wheat outside the CWB pool, through the use of spot and forward prices offered by the CWB;
- Restructure the governance of the CWB to enhance its accountability to farmers and to reflect modern corporate practice.

The Canadian federal government chose to ignore many of the WGMP's recommendations, including the first two.

In June 1998, the legislation to amend the Canadian Wheat Board Act known as Bill C-4 was passed by Canadian Parliament. The legislation, which in some contexts has been touted as a major step towards removing government control of the CWB, introduced only minor structural, administrative, and operational changes in the CWB. Bill C-4 provided for ten of the fifteen directors to be elected from producers. However, as was previously the case, the government continues to appoint five directors and the chief executive officer. In addition, the CWB now has expanded reporting responsibilities to both the Ministers of Agriculture and Finance. Clearly, under Bill C-4's provisions, the federal government retained critical elements of organizational control over the CWB that continued its role as a State Trading Enterprise. The CWB remains accountable to Parliament and not to farmers.

Under Bill C-4, only a few aspects of CWB operations were opened up. For example, the CWB now has greater flexibility in purchasing and paying for grain. Under Bill C-4, provisions were also made to establish a contingency fund from producer money to cover any losses on these new pricing options. Some evidence about the likely impacts of these new pricing provisions is provided by other producers' experiences with similar options. The Australian Wheat Board (AWB), for example, has offered similar pricing options for several years. However, producer interest has been low due to the unattractive level of the forward prices set by the AWB. The Ontario Wheat Producers' Marketing Board (OWPMB) offers producers alternative pricing options and pooling is not compulsory. The OWPMB operates about six different pools (segregated by class). In contrast, the CWB has only one pool for all classes of wheat (except durum) and appears to have chosen to pursue an approach similar to that of the AWB.

On balance, the changes under Bill C-4 in 1998 were relatively unimportant and largely cosmetic relative to the CWB's major functions. The amendments did not alter the compulsory single seller approach to marketing Canadian prairie wheat nor did they affect the lack of transparency surrounding the CWB's operations. They also failed to address several of the key recommendations from the Western Grain Marketing Panel. While the C-4 amendments were intended to make the CWB look less like a state trader, that objective has not been accomplished. Instead, there is more federal government oversight than before which could well attract greater scrutiny of the CWB under the WTO (Carter and Loyns, 1998).

A long-standing problem in the regulation and marketing of Canadian grains is the absence of credible economic analysis on important issues, particularly in relation to technological adaptation. There is no publicly available evidence of net economic benefits to producers and Canadians from the existence of the Canadian Grain Commission (formerly the Board of Grain Commissioners) and its "high quality wheat-only" regime. The Board of Grain Commissioners implemented the high quality policy in the 1920s. On the other hand, there is considerable economic analysis which argues Canada has missed important markets because of that emphasis (Canada Grains Council, 1982; Carter, Loyns and Ahmadi-Esfahani, 1986; Carter and Loyns, 1996; Klein, Webber, and Graham, 1986; Ulrich, Furtan and Schmitz, 1987). Similarly, there exists in the public domain only one study, conducted by the George Morris Institute (Martin, Mayer and Bouma), that purports to weigh the costs and the benefits of the Canadian Wheat Board. Kernel Visual Distinguishability (KVD), which has been around for generations, was finally exposed to a form of economic analysis in 2003 as a result of the CGC initiative to introduce a Variety Eligibility Declaration (VED) system (Canadian Grain Commission). It was the late 1970s before any significant economic impact analysis of the Crow rate regime began to surface. Conventional wisdom, or pure political expediency, has been the driver of the most important regulatory policy and programs in the Canadian grains industry.

Nor is the reaction by regulators to discount and disallow the contribution of new technology a new problem. In the 1970s, while other countries were selling wheat by protein designation, regulators in Canada were resisting the change. Even when sales (of only the top grades) were protein based at that time, producers did not receive the benefit in the form of a market signal (Loyns and Carter, 1984; Carter and Loyns, 1996). Similarly, semi-dwarf genetics, and different quality wheat did not gain any official acceptance until almost two decades after Canada's competitors had made the transition (Irvine; Carter and Loyns, 1996). In the malting barley market, there was resistance to importing US varieties but when B-1602 was introduced by the Prairie Pools in the eastern prairies in about 1988, the variety took off and became one of the most successful 6-row malting barley varieties ever produced. B-1602 still commands a premium. In 1998, an economic analysis of inland grain cleaning was finally conducted after generations of transporting dockage to port positions and often dumping or burning screenings, partly a consequence of subsidized freight rates (Grain Cleaning Consortium). Grade tolerances remain unnecessarily low today, causing over-cleaning of wheat for export.[15] And recently with fusarium head blight creating disease problems over at least the hog producing area of Manitoba, KVD and system integrity are keeping available seed stocks of fusarium resistant varieties from being grown under contracts with feed mills, with the result that feed mills and hog producers import US corn to avoid fusarium infected domestic feed.

These are only a few examples of the poor Canadian record on technological and market uptake in prairie grains. There are a number of common characteristics among these examples. They all derive from the official position that Canada's reputation for high quality wheat is absolute, despite compelling economic information that costs of this philosophy have been substantial; that the CWB in its closed and monopolistic form is needed to market wheat and barley in export channels despite the fact that other grains and agricultural products are exported without a domestic monopoly and in an open and transparent fashion; and despite, (more likely because of), failure of the system to undertake market and economic analysis to assess the rationale of the regulations.

In a recent speech, the CEO of the CWB, Mr. Measner[16] illustrated that this view persists

> *Like buyers of any well-branded, high-quality product, western Canadian wheat customers ... are willing to pay a premium for product quality and consistency* (p.3)

In this speech, Mr. Measner even took time to point out that the film star Sophia Loren eats special pasta made from 100% Canadian wheat. Would Ms. Loren not buy pasta made from Canadian wheat if it were not for the single-desk CWB?

It appears that the CWB is no longer making strong claims that it can exert market power over buyers. When discussing a single–desk, it is very important to distinguish price premiums due to wheat quality or particular services (such as favorable credit terms and protein over-deliveries) accompanying a sale, from those due to the exercise of monopoly power by a single seller (Carter and Loyns, 1996). The former is not necessarily due to a single–seller. Price premiums associated with special services built into a sale should be regarded as a return necessary to cover the costs of those services and not extra revenue due to the single–seller. Price premiums may also be due to factors other than the existence of market power. For example, Canadian grain quality standards and certification are usually said to add value to Canadian grain. Such premiums also would be available to private sellers and do not require a monopoly seller in order to be realized.

The regulatory system applied to grains, wheat in particular, has been more extensive than in other Canadian agricultural sectors;[17] it has been inflexible in the face of new commercial information; and it has been slow to change. Regulation, particularly in terms of payoff to grain standards and regulated marketing, has been perpetuated by top-down decision making, not market signals or economic analysis. Carter and Loyns addressed these issues in the closing comments of a book published by the University of Toronto Centre for Public Management (1998)....

> These market imperfections can be explained in large measure by a system that placed decision making power, but none of the commercial consequences, in the hands of a few regulators.
>
> Carter and Loyns, 1998; p.119.

Responsible public decisions have not been, and cannot be, made in this industry without careful objective economic analysis of options and consequences. Canada has repeatedly asserted its commitment to "science" as the basis for establishing health, safety and trade rules, and for settlement of trade disputes (Haddow). In the present case of GM wheat, where the issue is application of potentially significant technological contributions to prairie production, well beyond the matter of a particular herbicide tolerance, the dearth of analysis should be a matter of public concern. Claims by public agencies of impending market and environmental damage without evidence are irresponsible and potentially costly to the industry.

Canada and the prairies do not operate in isolation in terms of regulation as past experience has shown–including the costly delays in implementing protein segregation on the prairies, failure of the CWB to respond to growth in demand for different quality wheat, and indeed, from repeated use of US trade remedy laws to try to alter the CWB. Other countries are heavily involved in research to apply biotechnology to their most basic agricultural and food commodities (e.g., China, South Korea, and Japan). Although much is said in opposition to this form of technology in other countries, actions around the world, even in the EU, indicate that genetic modification of agricultural and food crops is moving ahead very rapidly. The "genie in the bottle" analogy has been overworked in this context, but the real bottled genie is about which nations will be first to capture innovator benefits in GM wheat and other food grains.

Segregation Concerns

If GM wheat is licensed in Canada, there will be a transition period of a few years to allow acreage to expand and reach an equilibrium level based on market conditions. Initially the GM wheat will most likely be handled through a closed loop system, as outlined by the Grain Industry Working Group on Genetically Modified Wheat. This mechanism was used initially for GM canola in Canada and it was successful. However, it is no longer necessary to segregate bulk non-GM from GM canola as most customers do not care. Those who do care have gone to containers and there is now a small trade volume in containerized canola. Today, apart from the containerized trade, there is no world price premium for non-GM canola (Foster, Berry and Hogan).

Australia initially rejected GM canola, partly in anticipation of earning price premiums for non-GM canola, but this never materialized in the marketplace. As a result, in 2003 the Australian Federal Government approved two varieties of herbicide resistant GM canola for commercial production–the first real GM food crop to be approved in Australia.[18] In retrospect, the Australian government's strategy of waiting to approve GM canola was costly for the Australian growers. An Australian government report (Stone, Matysek, and Dolling) found that Australian grain and oilseed growers stood to lose if they continued to reject GM technology.[19] They concluded that if Australia did not adopt GM crops as fast as most of their competitors did, then Australia would lose market shares over time, both in its primary crop markets and in downstream food product markets.

After the initial transition period for the introduction of GM wheat in

Canada, there will be a movement away from the closed loop system to keep marketing costs down. A system of segregating non-GM wheat may then develop if there is a sufficient demand for non-GM wheat, and some customers are willing to pay a price premium. The relative importance of this demand for non-GM wheat will be partly determined by the market, but heavily influenced by foreign government policy on GM labeling and tolerance levels.

Japan and the United Kingdom (UK) are two importers that may be willing to pay a premium for non-GM wheat. Japan is a large wheat importer, accounting for about 10% of the CWB's annual sales to domestic and foreign customers. The UK is a much smaller market for Canada, typically buying about 2% of total CWB sales each year.

Suppose that for a portion of their imports, Japan and the UK are willing to pay a non-GM price premium, as segregation will add value in the minds of Japanese and UK customers. This is quite likely because Japan now imports over 500,000 mt of non-GM soybeans annually from the US and Canada, and a similar amount from Brazil and China. Although there are no official data, up to 20% of Japan's annual soybean imports (of 5 mmt) may be non-GM. The non-GM soybeans are mainly used for tofu, which unlike soybean oil, is subject to Japan's GM labeling regulations. In Japan, tofu consumers prefer non-GM; otherwise the consumers will not buy it. In addition, Japan imports some non-GM corn each year from the US and China. This corn is used in food products (such as snack food) that are subject to the GM labeling rules and the processors want to avoid labeling, as in the case of tofu. Most of Japan's imported corn is GM, which is used for animal feed and the final meat product does not have to be labeled.

StarLink is a biotech variety of corn that was approved by the US Environmental Protection Agency (EPA) in 1998 for commercial production for animal feed but not for human consumption (i.e., a split license). StarLink was not approved for human consumption because it contained Cry9C, a protein that might cause allergic reactions in some humans. The US grain handling system was not prepared to handle the split licensing of StarLink (Uchtmann) and as a result StarLink easily became co-mingled with non-StarLink corn and found its way into US and foreign food products and bulk export cargoes. In September 2000, traces of StarLink were detected in taco shells in the US and this led to recalls of hundreds of food products domestically and overseas. The split EPA license was clearly flawed regulation and this experience has adversely affected worldwide public acceptance of bio-engineered crops.

The StarLink contamination was disruptive because a relatively large share of the market had zero tolerance for its use, and zero tolerance is impossible to attain (Lin, Price, and Allen). StarLink zero tolerance applied to food use of corn in the US, Japan and South Korea. In addition, Japan had zero tolerance for feed use of StarLink.

The attempt to isolate StarLink after the contamination provided a real-world experiment on the costs of segregation. Once co-mingling of StarLink was discovered, about 20 to 25% of the market for US corn required assurance that they were purchasing non-StarLink. Lin, Price, and Allen estimated that the costs of segregating non-biotech corn could run between 18 and 22¢ (US) per bushel. However, after the StarLink incident they found that price differences between StarLink and StarLink-free corn under the IP program ranged from 7 to 12¢ (US) per bushel. This cost is surprisingly small for a zero tolerance segregation program, and it illustrates that segregation of bulk-handled grains is feasible even when the tolerance level for accidental mixing is extremely low.

Independent of the StarLink incident, trade sources report that the total cost of segregating non-GM corn and soybeans ranges from 10 to 20¢ (US) per bushel, with soybeans closer to 10¢ and corn closer to 20¢. In some cases, the grain companies are segregating by variety anyway and so the segregation cost of non-GM products is not particularly high.

For CWB grains, the kernel visual distinguishability (KVD) system means that segregation of wheat by variety is very uncommon in Canada and is discouraged. This may explain why the Warburton program[20] initially met with strong resistance from the CWB. A spokesman for the Canadian flour millers explains:

> the current varietal licensing system that permits varieties to be included in these classes of wheat that are segregated in Canada actually makes varietal segregation and identity preservation virtually unnecessary for our industry. It's not an exciting thing for us to have people talk about IP and segregation by variety. It's not an advantage.
>
> Mr. Gordon Harrison (President, Canadian National Millers Association) testimony to Standing Committee on Agriculture and Agri-Food, 37th Parliament, 2nd Session, April 3, 2003.

This quote and the opposition of the Canadian flour millers to the 2003 Canadian Grain Commission's Variety Eligibility Declaration[21] (VED) proposal underscores the fact that the Canadian grain handling system is out of sync with other parts of the developed world when it comes to sourcing grain by variety. Variety specific origination of grains and oilseeds is actually quite common and is growing in North America and Europe (e.g., wheat in US for General Mills and Nabisco Brands Inc., corn in US for ethanol, non-GM corn and soybeans in the US for Japan, non-GM soybeans in the EU for bread flour, containerized canola into the EU, wheat in the UK for Rank Hovis, oats in North America for General Mills, etc.). General Mills (the second largest cereal manufacturer in the US) aims to identity preserve 100% of their grain purchases by 2007. A General Mills vice-president (Ronald Olson) stated:

> *If you can get rid of differing varieties in grains, then you can get better quality.*
> Quoted in *Milling and Baking News*, June 19, 2001, p.26.

These examples strongly imply that segregation creates value for the customer, and this is why they are willing to pay the extra costs of producing and sorting crops by variety.

Another important consideration is tolerance levels for accidental mixing of grain varieties. In the case of non-GM, some foreign buyers require more stringent tolerance levels than the official government levels. For instance, the commercial reality for some grain companies is a 1.0% tolerance level in Japan, considerably more rigid than the Japanese government's official tolerance level of 5%. As mentioned above, typical segregation fees are about 10¢ per bushel on soybeans to meet the 1.0% tolerance. On corn, there is greater risk due to the lingering effects of the StarLink incident, as Japan has continued to monitor inbound corn shipments for StarLink. Because there remains a small amount of StarLink in the system, corn requires more testing compared to soybeans and this has increased the cost of corn segregation to 15¢ to 20¢ per bushel. In some cases there are rejections of shipments to Japan, and these are rectified through further blending or redirecting the shipment. The Warburton wheat program has also successfully dealt with rejected shipments.

Based on interviews with those involved in the Warburton program and with traders who now service the Japanese market for non-GM corn and soybeans, we believe Canadian exporters could successfully sort non-GM wheat to tolerance levels of 5% or lower. This segregation would involve bulk wheat and would be based on farmer affidavits and overlapping testing. The total cost would run less than 15¢ per bushel, for a 3 to 5% tolerance level. Wilson and Dahl estimate 15¢ per bu (USD) for wheat. See

Table 1.2 for alternative estimates. It is worth noting that export cargoes of Canadian wheat destined for Japan are now thoroughly tested for pesticide residue, as part of Japan's Food Agency requirement. More than 100 different chemicals are tested for, at a cost of about 1¢ per bushel, paid for by the Japanese importers.

Table 1.2. Estimates of Segregation Costs for GM wheat

	Estimated Segregation Costs
Carter, Berwald & Loyns, 2005	7 to 11¢/bu ($Cdn)
Taylor et al., 2003	6¢/bu ($US)
Gosnell, 2002	5 to 15¢/bu ($Cdn)

Japan can easily afford to pay a small premium to avoid GM wheat (at least initially) and they may have no choice because some of their own domestic customers have stated that they do not want GM wheat. For example, Japan's Flour Millers Association has stated that GM wheat will not be accepted in the Japanese market. The Japanese Ministry of Agriculture's Food Agency makes a huge profit from its control over wheat imports. It resells imported wheat to domestic Japanese mills at approximately double the world price, basis Japan. If the Food Agency is willing to pay a premium for non-GM wheat (say 5% of the $5 per bushel cif price–or 25¢ per bu.), this may have no impact on the actual price paid by domestic millers. The small price premium for non-GM would simply come out of the profits earned by the Food Agency on wheat imports, estimated to be about $5.40 per bu., or $1.2 billion per year.

The CWB has indicated that meeting a 5% tolerance level, as in Japan, may not be too costly:

> We market varieties of malting barley, and we market varieties of wheat within larger classes. We try to hit a 95% purity level, so that's a 5% tolerance level. That seems to be something we can do in a fairly economical and foolproof way, but 1% would be very difficult.
> Ms. Patty Rosher, Program Manager, Market Development, CWB, testimony to Standing Committee on Agriculture and Agri-Food, 37th Parliament, 1st Session, Nov. 1, 2001.

Some previous research (Furtan Gray and Holzman) has suggested that segregation of GM wheat would be too expensive to be practical. We strongly disagree and point out that Canadian agriculture has plenty of examples of segregation and IP programs in existence today. The CWB can and does segregate grain shipments now, with at least 65 segregations for wheat. Existing segregation programs in Canadian grains include:

1. Seed production;
2. High acid rapeseed;
3. Malting barley varieties;
4. The CWB's Warburton wheat program;
5. Non-GM soybean sales to Japan; and
6. Special CWB contracts.

The costs of these various segregation programs vary considerably, depending on geographic production patterns, volumes traded, and allowable tolerance levels. The segregation costs range from around 2% of the farmgate price, up to 10% or more.

GM Labeling and Tolerance for Accidental Mixing

The European Union (EU) is doing its best to prevent the further introduction of biotech crops in Europe or elsewhere. This fight between the United States and the EU is now being played out at the World Trade Organization (WTO). In the spring of 2003, the US filed a high profile WTO case against the EU over its embargo on the approval of any new genetically modified crops, in place since 1998. Canada supported the US initiative, although the CWB tried to convince the Canadian government not to back the US on this issue. The US may also bring a case to the WTO over the EU's stringent GM labeling regulations.[22]

Some observers believe the US is simply trying to bully the EU into accepting GM crops so multinational seed companies can benefit. Others argue that the issues surrounding transgenic crops give environmental activists like Greenpeace and Friends of the Earth something to protest over. They believe the Greens are holding the EU politicians captive on the transgenic issue and unduly influencing EU biotech policy. But the US may win the WTO case because this case is similar to the disagreement won by the US in the late 1990s over the EU's ban on hormone treated beef imports. Under the WTO's agreement on sanitary and phytosanitary measures (SPS), non-tariff barriers like the EU embargo on GM crops would have to be scientifically justified, which is not possible based on current scientific research.

The EU parliament does not pretend that GM food products pose a health risk. Instead, European politicians talk about the environmental risk of GM crops, despite the lack of scientific evidence of significant environmental risks. Given that GM crops are environmentally friendly, it is ironic that environmental groups are leading the anti-GM charge in Europe and elsewhere. Biotech crops reduce the use of chemicals and encourage zero-till farming, helping to conserve the soil. The introduction of GM cotton, corn and soybeans has been a tremendous benefit for the natural environment in the US The National Center for Food and Agricultural Policy[23] estimated that in 2001, GM crops currently produced in the US reduced annual pesticide use by 46 million total pounds and improved annual farm income by $1.5 billion. Western Europe is one of the heaviest agricultural users of chemicals on the globe, and moving towards GM crops would cut this down.

In the 1990s, the EU approved some GM varieties of corn, soybeans and rapeseed, but then suddenly halted the approval process in 1998. The EU has offered no scientific evidence in support of its prohibition on new GM crops. As a result, the US maintains that the ban constitutes an illegal trade barrier under the WTO and that it restricts imports of US corn in particular. The EU's response is that they are in the process of lifting the moratorium and therefore the WTO case is unnecessary.

In fact, the WTO case symbolizes a bigger issue because many developing countries are afraid to research and approve GM crops for fear of jeopardizing trade relations with the EU. Furthermore, even if the EU moratorium is lifted, the EU's GM labeling regulations will serve as a second line of defense against imports. The US first exported GM food to Europe in 1996. It was tomato puree from California and it was voluntarily labeled as genetically engineered. The product was a big hit with consumers in Britain because it was cheaper than conventional tomato puree. However when GM soybeans were imported into Europe later that year, there was a huge political backlash from environmental groups and the EU was then quick to introduce mandatory labeling for GM foods, which took hold in 1997.

In the official response to the WTO case, the EU said that the lack of consumer demand accounts for the low sales of GM products in the EU. The EU parliament maintains that their labeling regulations are in place to give consumers information and to provide them with options. But the EU's approach to mandatory labeling of GM food is not really giving consumers a choice because you cannot find GM food products on retail shelves in Europe. It is hard to argue against the importance of consumer choice, but in fact consumers in Europe do not really have a choice, as food processors and retailers there have moved away from using GM ingredients in response to the stringent labeling laws. Furthermore, a substantial amount of GM food eaten in the EU and Japan doesn't have to be labeled. These products include cheese, soya sauce, some baked goods and numerous manufactured foods.

European food manufacturers and retailers have taken very strong positions against GM foods. This is especially true in the UK, where retailers were one of the first in Europe to seek out GM-free foods. The BSE factor was one reason that UK consumers were more aware of food safety concerns. The manufacturers and retailers have played to this fear and they have used biotech fears as a marketing tool. Kalaitzandonakes and Bijman have found that food retailers and manufacturers are acting out of economic self-interest, rather than simply responding to consumer interests.

This is precisely why the US government views the EU's mandatory labeling policy as a trade barrier. Japan also has mandatory GM food labeling but Japan's policy is not of great concern to the US because it is much more practical than the EU approach. Japan is a large net food importer and therefore cannot afford to use labeling policy to turn away grain imports from the US.

Any decision on labeling of GM food presents major challenges for policy makers. The most fundamental problem relates to DNA detection, because the measurement of GM material becomes difficult or impossible if the GM crop is highly processed. For example, products such as soybean oil or meat produced from GM feedstuffs do not contain any evident GM protein. In addition, biotechnology that is used in certain food and beverage manufacturing processes cannot easily be detected in the final product.

Internationally, the Codex Alimentarius Commission, an international standards setting body for food, has a Committee on Food Labeling. Since 1990, Codex has sought to develop guidelines for labeling biotech foods. So far, however, there is no agreement on the international standards. In all likelihood, a final Codex standard on the labeling of biotech foods will not occur for many years.

The approaches taken in different countries towards GM food labeling differ greatly (Sheldon; Carter and Gruère 2003a) as shown on Table 1.3. The EU has very strict GM labeling guidelines. In contrast are the United States, Argentina, and Canada, the three big GM producers, whose governments do not believe in mandatory labeling. The US government's non-support for mandatory labeling reflects the scientific evidence by the US Food and Drug Administration (FDA) that GM foods are nutritionally equivalent to non-GM foods. As long as the food is safe from impurities, labeling is not needed. Japan, South Korea, China, and other countries are between the EU and the United States on this issue.

Under EU labeling regulations, which became more stringent in 2004, food manufacturers must label all ingredients produced from GM material, irrespective of whether or not the GM material is detectable in the final product.[24] Furthermore, all animal feed from GM soybeans or corn must be labeled, which is significant given the widespread use of GM soymeal in the EU.

Table 1.3. Sample of International Guidelines for Labeling of GM Foods

	Labeling Scheme	% Threshold for Unintended GM Material	Are Some Biotech Foods and Processes Exempt?
Canada	Voluntary	5%	N/A
United States	Voluntary [a]	N/A	N/A
Argentina	Voluntary	N/A	N/A
Australia & New Zealand	Mandatory	1%	Yes
European Union	Mandatory	0.9%	Yes
Japan	Mandatory	5% [b]	Yes
S. Korea	Mandatory	3% [b]	Yes
Indonesia	Mandatory	5% [c]	Yes
China	Mandatory	0%	Yes
Russia	Mandatory	5%	Yes

N/A means not applicable
a. The US voluntary guidelines are technically still in draft form. They are available at http://www.cfsan.fda.gov/~dms/biolabgu.html.
b. Top 3 ingredients in Japan and top 5 ingredients in S. Korea.
c. Not yet operational.

Source: Personal interviews and various Attaché Reports from the USDA Foreign Agricultural Service (http://www.fas.usda.gov/itp/biotech/countries.html).

As shown in Table 1.3, if any single food product ingredient contains more than 0.9% "approved" GM material, then the final product must be labeled in the EU. Adventitious presence of unapproved GM material that has received a favorable risk evaluation from the EU may be present up to a maximum of 0.5%. Unapproved GM material that has not been through the EU risk evaluation process has a tolerance of 0%, which is virtually impossible to meet, as is evidenced by the StarLink corn incident in the United States.

The Japanese government requires mandatory labeling when GM material is present in the top three raw ingredients and accounts for 5% or more of the total weight. It also admits the presence of non-GM labels at the same tolerance level, if produced with identity preservation. Tofu can be made from non-GM soybeans and be labeled as such or else it must be labeled as containing GM material. Exemptions to Japan's labeling requirements include feedstuffs, alcoholic beverages, and processed foods such as soya sauce, corn flakes, and other vegetable oils. South Korea's regulations are similar to Japan's except the tolerance level is 3% of the top 5 ingredients. Unlike in Korea and Japan, in the EU the threshold applies to each ingredient.

China leads the world in public biotech crop research (Huang et al.). GM crops in the field trial stage in China include rice, wheat, corn, soybeans, potatoes, cabbage, and tobacco. GM cotton accounted for about 60% of China's cotton acreage in 2003. China has taken a firm position on GM labeling, but such legislation will be difficult to enforce.

For a time China introduced restrictions on GM soybean imports. Outside China, this was viewed as a trade barrier that limited soybean imports from the United States. These restrictions were lifted in 2004. China's position towards biotechnology in agriculture appears to be heavily influenced by EU policy. Also, Greenpeace has recently opened an office in China where they are testing foods in China and at the border for GM traits. Greenpeace is also active in testing food products in Russia for genetically modified organisms.

In 2004, Canada introduced voluntary labeling for GM foods.[25] The system allows food manufacturers to label their products as GM-free as long as they contain no more than 5% transgenic materials. The Canadian guidelines are similar to those in the United States, where the US Food and Drug Administration (FDA) has produced guidelines for the food processing industry. Food processors may voluntarily label either the presence or absence of a genetically engineered food in their products as long as the information is accurate. The main difference between the Canadian and US guidelines is that the US FDA does not provide guidance on the threshold level for adventitious presence of bioengineered material.

So why do we observe the wide difference in approaches to GM labeling across countries? There are several possible explanations. The EU and Japan have experienced domestic food scares in recent years. Consumers in these countries do not believe scientists and politicians who say GM food is safe. Political pressure from environmental groups plays on this fear and raises unscientific concerns about GM food safety (Bernauer and Meins).

On a larger scale, labeling affects international trade. Consequently, the European policy affects the choices of other agricultural exporting countries. Australian GM policies were partially designed to fit the labeling requirement for exports to the EU and Japan. Eastern European countries and Russia have most likely decided to follow the EU's labeling requirements for trade reasons. Those eastern European countries planning to join the EU really have no choice.

Potential Economic Impacts of GM Wheat
Wheat is a struggling industry in North America and elsewhere. As a result, wheat acreage in Canada has been shifting to other more profitable crops (see chapter 2 for more details), and importers are turning to other non-traditional export suppliers, such as the former Soviet Union. In the United States, wheat acreage has also fallen quite dramatically–declining by 28 million acres or nearly one-third from its peak in 1981. Despite claims by the Canadian Wheat Board a decade ago that important wheat import markets were highly dependent on Canadian wheat, and could not substitute away from Canadian western red spring (CWRS), Canada's market share has fallen dramatically in some key markets. Brazil is the largest net wheat importer in the world and Canada's share of that market is now near zero, down from close to 30 percent in the early 1990s. Ironically, Brazil was listed by the CWB as one of ten key markets "at-risk" if GM wheat were to be introduced in Canada (Kuntz).

The world wheat market is very dynamic and competitive, as the past few years have clearly demonstrated. For instance, the CWB wheat pool ran a deficit in 2002-03 despite some very high prices early in the crop year. Growth in overall world trade is stagnant and Canada is facing increased competition from expanded production in Argentina, Eastern Europe, and central Asia. Therefore the Canadian industry should carefully consider the benefits and costs of GM wheat, as adoption of this new technology may be necessary to keep prairie wheat farms competitive internationally. If GM wheat is not first adopted in North America, the developing world (e.g., China or Iran) may be the first to take up this technology, which will marginalize the Canadian wheat industry even further. China is not taking a back seat in bioengineered crop research. China has a major ongoing research program on biotech rice and other crops such as wheat, and is predicted to be an early adopter (Brookes and Barfoot).

For the past several years, canola has been more profitable than wheat for Canadian prairie growers. This is partly due to the advantages of biotech canola, which saves growers input costs and boosts yields. Over 90% of the canola acreage in Canada is planted to herbicide tolerant varieties, and over 70% of the canola acreage is planted to varieties created with recombinant DNA technology; the benefits to the prairie economy of this relatively new technology are significant. A 2001 study found that GM canola increased average yields by 10%, lowered herbicide use by 40%, reduced the number of field operations on each farm, and produced a higher quality crop with less dockage. Overall, the estimated net benefits to growers associated with adopting GM canola are between $5.80 and $10.62 per acre (Serecon Management Consulting).

To put the potential economic impacts of GM wheat in perspective with other crops, Table 1.4 reports a range of representative estimates of the economic effects of alternative biotech crops. Two literature review papers (Marra, Pardey, and Alston; Gianessi, et al.) are included in Table 1.4, both of which report information from previous studies. A number of alternative methodologies are represented in the summary statistics in Table 1.4, so the number and type of reported economic indicator varies somewhat. For example, McBride and Brooks use paired mean tests to analyze survey data, Annou, Wailes, and Cramer use the ex-ante partial budgeting approach, and Benbrook uses field trial data to generate impact estimates. The range of estimates in Table 1.4 reflects potential differences between regions, but overall they provide the likely magnitude of the economic impacts of adopting biotech crops.

The studies represented in Table 1.4 suggest that Bt cotton offers the largest economic gain per acre (ranging from $12.20 to $173), followed by herbicide tolerant (HT) cotton, Bt corn, HT canola, and HT soybeans. To date, HT rice and HT wheat are not being commercially grown anywhere in the world. However, the studies reported in Table 1.4 show

Table 1.4. Estimated Economic Impacts of Selected Transgenic Crop Cultivation from the Economics Literature

Crop	Authors	Change in Yield	Change in Pesticide Use	Change in Returns ($ per Acre)
HT Canola	Marra, et. al. (2002)	-1.9 to 24.5 bu/acre	—	$11.30
	Gianessi, et. al. (2002)	6% to 10%	-55% a.i./acre	$12.65 to $18.00
	Serecon Management Inc. (2001)	10%	-40%	$5.80 to $10.62
Bt Corn	Marra, et. al. (2002)	6.7 to 18.2 bu/acre	—	$23.40 to $60.10
	Gianessi, et. al. (2002)	0 to 40 bu/acre	-0.38 to -0.175 lbs/acre	-$2.50 to $73.50
	Benbrook (2001)	mixed	—	-$2.16 to $1.68 / bu
Bt Cotton	Marra, et. al. (2002)	-79 to 325 lbs lint/acre	-3.4 to -1.3 applications	$16.50 to $173.00
	Gianessi, et. al. (2002)	-1 to 144 lbs lint/acre	-3.4 to -0.4 applications	$12.20 to $63.00
	McBride and Brooks (2000)	0[a]	-0.61 to 0 applications	$19.72 to $34.25[c]
	Fernandez-Cornejo & McBride (2000)	increase	decrease to no change	increase
HT Cotton	Marra, et. al. (2002)	-163.7 to 120.0 lbs lint/acre	—	$17.10 to $108.00
	Gianessi, et. al. (2002)	no change	decrease	$8.00 to $150.00
	McBride and Brooks (2000)	-10% to 0%	-2.75 to 0 applications	0[a]
	Fernandez-Cornejo & McBride (2000)	increase	0[a]	increase
HT Rice	Gianessi, et. al. (2002)	—	-5.85 to -1.62 lbs/acre	$21.00 to $90.00
	Annou, et. al. (2000)	-10% to 20%	—	-$24.99 to $50.32

Table 1.4. Estimated Economic Impacts of Selected Transgenic Crop Cultivation from the Economics Literature

Crop	Authors	Change in Yield	Change in Pesticide Use	Change in Returns ($ per Acre)
HT Soybean	Marra, et. al. (2002)	-4.4 to 2.7 bu/acre	—	$14.00
	Gianessi, et. al. (2002)	8% to 13%	-1.3 to 0.60 lbs a.i./acre	$2.29 to $36.70
	McBride and Brooks (2000)	13% to 18%	-1.68 to -0.73 applications	0[a]
	Fernandez-Cornejo & McBride (2000)	small increase	mixed	0[a]
HT Spring Wheat	Taylor, deVuyst, Koo (2003)	10%	-$2/acre	$7.75[b, d],
	Gianessi, et. al. (2002)	0 to 4 bu/acre	-$9.50/acre	$9.50 to $21.50[b]
	Furtan et al. (2003b)	3%	not reported	13.88[b]
	Holzman (2001)	2 to 10%	-$16.45/acre	$18.89 to $28.67[b]
	Carter, Berwald and Loyns (2005)	5 to 13%	-$16.45/acre	$13.06 to $27.97[b]

Notes: With the exception of Gianessi et al., the estimated change in returns for HT spring wheat are in $Cdn. Serecon Management's estimate for HT canola is also in $Cdn. a.i. denotes active ingredient. [a] Change is not statistically significant. [b] Does not include technology fee for transgenic seed. [c] Seed and pest control costs only. [d] Estimate for Canada only.

Table 1.4: continued

Annou, M., E. Wailes, and G. Cramer: An ex-ante estimate of per-acre benefits of adopting transgenic rice in Arkansas, using a partial budgeting approach. Change in grower returns includes -10% to 10% yield change and $0 to $25/acre tech fee.

Benbrook, C. : An independent, but not peer reviewed, report that discusses pricing, yields, and economic impacts of Bt corn in the United States. Yield data from various Midwest corn varietal trials in 2000, and economic returns calculated by quantifying value of yield loss avoided less seed price premiums by State for 1996-2001.

Carter, C.A., D. Berwald, and A. Loyns (see Chapter 4 below): Uses similar approach to Holzman but added two additional soil zones. The numbers presented in this table are the static results for the black soil zone. This permits direct comparison with Holzman. For more details see Chapter 4 below.

Gianessi et al.: A collection of literature reviews and analysis organized around 40 case studies selected through literature searches and personal interviews of researchers. Return estimates are changes in total revenue minus variable costs.

Fernandez-Cornejo, J. and W. D. McBride.: An econometric model estimated from the 1997 USDA ARMS data. Elasticities are calculated for pesticide use, crop yields, and net returns. "Small increase" is a statistically significant elasticity with respect to increases in the probability of adoption of less than 0.1, "increase" is an elasticity greater than 0.1 but less than 0.5, "decrease" is defined as an elasticity less than -0.1 but greater than -0.5, and "no change" is a statistically insignificant elasticity estimate.

Furtan, W.H., R.S. Gray, and J.J. Holzman (2003b): Presented as part of their work on the option value of introducing herbicide tolerant wheat, the details of their calculations are not reported. The information on the benefits at the farm level is primarily from the work of Holzman. The numbers reported here do not include the estimate by Furtan, Gray and Holzman (2003a) that wheat prices would fall by 75 to 80¢ ($US) if GM was introduced in North America.

Holzman, J.: Considers the costs and benefits of introducing HT wheat. The numbers presented here are what Holzman refers to as "static" benefits, which do not include the production costs of other crops in the rotation. If those are included, the benefits are lower, ranging from -$ 2.40 to $7.38 per acre.

Table 1.4: continued

Marra, M., P. Pardey, and J. Alston: A literature survey of farm-level impacts, including mean, minimum, and maximum measures for yields, profits, and pesticide use. The ranges from Marra et al. presented here are based on the minimum and maximum "mean" values presented in Tables 1-3 of Marra, et. al. Return estimates include cost of transgenic seed.

McBride, W. D. and N. Brooks: Provides statistical analysis of 1997 USDA Agricultural Resource Management Study (ARMS) data using differences of means test between transgenic and traditional technologies for United States geographic regions. Soybean regions were the Corn Belt, Lake States, Southeast, Delta, and Northern Plains. Cotton regions were Southeast, Delta, Southern Plains, and Southwest. Authors suggest caution in interpretation of results, as control for all other aspects of the agricultural system with farm survey data is impossible. Per acre returns are calculated as differences in seed and pest control costs.

Serecon Management: Surveyed 600 canola farmers and completed 12 grower case studies in western Canada. Estimated economic impacts of GM canola with crop budgeting models.

Taylor, R.D., E.A. DeVuyst, and W.W. Koo: They use a spatial equilibrium model to evaluate impacts of introducing GM wheat. The model is calibrated to historical data and alternative scenarios are analyzed, where they vary production regions and adoption rates. Scenario 8 is reported here, where GM wheat production is allowed in all spring wheat growing regions of Canada and the US, with a 10% yield increase.

potential grower benefits per acre from GM rice and wheat are similar to gains for HT canola and HT soybeans. Farm level gains are potentially higher for HT rice than HT wheat, according to Table 1.4.

The farm level estimated revenue gains from biotech canola and soybeans are at the lower end of the spectrum of dollar gains per acre reported in Table 1.4. This is interesting because the actual adoption rates for canola and soybeans are at the high end of the range in North America (see Table 1.1 for adoption rates). In the US, the HT soybean adoption rate is approximately 81% of total acres, compared to 73% for (HT and Bt) cotton, and 40% for (HT and Bt) corn–accounting for stacked traits in cotton and corn. For all these biotech crops, the adoption rates have continued to increase each year.

There are many possible explanations as to why the adoption rate in corn is lower than for soybeans and cotton, even though the economic estimates suggest the potential grower gains per acre are higher for corn from adoption. These explanations include EU trade barriers (fewer approved biotech corn varieties), regional differences in pest and weed problems that may not give biotech varieties an advantage in every region, and possible errors in the economic estimates.

The estimated gains associated with adopting HT wheat range from approximately $7.55 to over $28 per acre. These estimates do not include a technology fee, so the farmer gains would be lower by the amount of this fee. Using Roundup Ready® corn and soybeans, a single-gene technology currently on the market, as a reference point; the technology fee is approximately thirty to sixty percent of conventional seed costs per acre (Annou, Wailes, and Cramer). This would put the technology fee for wheat in a range of approximately $4 to $7.50 per acre.

Most of these studies use a similar partial budgeting approach, which is reasonable because GM wheat is not commercially grown so there are no data outside the field trials. Our estimate is also based on partial budgeting and in Chapter 4 we build on the model used by Holzman. In addition, we use the option value approach recommended by the CWB's Industry Working Group on GM Wheat and employed by Furtan, Gray and Holzman (2003b).

Our estimates of the farm-level benefits of adopting HT wheat are similar to those of Holzman, because they were based on his work. Although the estimates of Furtan, Gray and Holzman (2003b) were also based on

Holzman, the benefits they report are much lower (by as much as $15 per acre) than Holzman's or our own. All of the studies on HT wheat in Table 1.4 indicate a large potential farm level benefit associated with adoption. The benefits are primarily from cost savings; for example, even if there was no yield increase from HT wheat, cost savings are estimated at over $10 per acre. Yield gains from adopting HT wheat further increase the benefits at the farm level.

Furtan, Gray and Holzman (2003b) use the *real options* approach to decision-making in their paper, and the CWB's Industry Working Group has also endorsed this method. Briefly, the real options approach considers both uncertainty and the irreversibility of the decision to introduce GM wheat. Due to these factors, the benefits/cost ratio of adopting GM wheat must be above a "threshold" level before adoption is a good idea. This requirement is more stringent than the traditional benefit-cost framework because it sets a higher standard.

Implicitly the overall economic impact of GM wheat introduction at the farm level depends on key issues discussed in this report, such as market demand and segregation. The market demand for non-GM wheat determines whether non-GM wheat will sell at a price premium. Segregation of GM and conventional wheat is also important, because if it is too costly, it could eliminate the benefits of adoption at the farm level. Our estimates suggest that after accounting for the market impacts and segregation costs, immediate adoption of GM wheat is optimal. The only other work to date on the issue is that of Furtan, Gray, and Holzman (2003b). They suggest that the benefit/cost ratio is not yet at the threshold level, so adoption should be postponed, primarily due to the fact that they calculate smaller farm level benefits than Holzman or we do.

Furtan, Gray, and Holzman (2003b) do not discuss when adoption should take place, if not now. If future research leads to higher future benefits from GM wheat, as they suggest, then the decision to introduce GM wheat should be revisited, and the new benefit/cost ratio should be tested against the real options threshold. Our results suggest the threshold is already met, while the work of Furtan, Gray, and Holzman (2003b) implies that the threshold will be attained in the near future.

Our detailed estimates of the economic benefits are reported in Chapter 4. Besides the yield and cost assumptions, the estimated benefits at the grower level depend on the soil zone, whether or not zero-till is practiced, and the specifics of crop rotation. We assume a $7/acre technology fee and a 9% yield advantage with GM wheat and these assumptions are allowed to vary through sensitivity analysis. We believe that 9% is a conservative estimate of the yield advantage associated with GM wheat as Kidnie et al. report Canadian field trial data from 2000 through 2002 that show a GM wheat yield advantage ranging from 9% to 14%. Blackshaw and Harker report field trial data for 2000 and 2001 in Alberta, which show a mean yield increase of about 9% for GM wheat compared to conventional wheat.

The most plausible estimates of grower benefits range from about $9 to $18 per acre for the static (i.e., one-year) analysis. With multiple years and rotation considerations, the benefits are typically lower due to costs of controlling volunteer GM wheat. The estimated benefits range from about $5.50 to $17.00 per acre, with rotations and after accounting for the technology fee.

Using the real options approach, we find the benefit-cost ratio far exceeds the threshold level. This suggests that GM wheat should be adopted on the prairies as soon as it has food, feed, and environmental approval in North America and Japan. The estimated annual net benefits from adoption to all Canadian wheat growers are about $287 million per year.

Conclusion

Despite the rapid and successful adoption of genetically modified (GM) canola in western Canada since 1996, there is a surprisingly significant amount of opposition to the commercialization of GM wheat in Canada. This led to a decision by Monsanto in the spring of 2004 to shelve its GM wheat program. New technology in agriculture often provokes resistance, especially from government bureaucracies and commercial firms (such as food processors) that may be comfortable with the *status quo*. For instance, despite the obvious economic advantages, the movement from bagged wheat to bulk handling was resisted in Australia for over thirty years before bulk handling was finally introduced after the First World War. To give another example, in many corners of the globe there was resistance to the Green Revolution and its high yielding semi-dwarf varieties introduced in the late 1960s, even though it helped greatly to alleviate world hunger and improved farm returns in many nations, including returns in Canada.

Critics of GM wheat in Canada make reference to losses that Canadian farmers may have suffered due to lost European markets from the introduction of

GM canola in western Canada. While it is the case the EU had been a significant market for Canadian canola in some years prior to the introduction of GM canola, it was an erratic importer. More importantly, Canada's exports of GM canola to China, Japan and Mexico have been strong and reached record levels in recent years. There is no question that GM canola has been a major success for the prairie agricultural industry, including producers.

However, Canadian domestic vested interests alone do not fully explain the negative views towards GM wheat. In this chapter we explain why the commercialization of GM wheat in Canada involves different market issues than in the case of GM canola. Wheat plays a much greater role in world food markets than canola (or other GM crops for that matter) so the introduction of GM wheat will have a larger impact on farmers and consumers around the world.

Governments, food companies, and environmental activists in Japan and the European Union have rallied against GM wheat. In this opposition, politics plays a greater role than science. The mandatory labeling policies in the EU and Japan have resulted in the virtual disappearance of any labeled GM product from their food shelves. As a consequence, consumers do not have a choice, and the label has acted as a "ban" of GM foods. This ban will impact GM wheat heavily because almost all wheat products would require labeling. In contrast, some canola, corn and soybean products, although GM, are exempt from labeling requirements. In the case of wheat, biotech fears among consumers will be used as a marketing tool by food retailers in Europe and Japan. Compared to canola or soybeans, it will be easier to test for GM wheat in food products, so attention will be drawn to wheat and this plays into the hands of the environmental activist groups. In essence, the EU wants GM producers and exporters to "pay" for any labeling and segregation costs.

Europe (i.e., UK) and Japan are the tail that wags the dog when it comes to Canada's wheat markets. These two customers combined account for only about 12 percent of CWB annual sales of hard red spring wheat, yet they have tremendous influence over the CWB mindset. But politics in these two markets and associated biotech fears should not dictate whether or not prairie farmers adopt GM wheat. After all, the EU is one of the CWB's major competitors in world wheat markets. Canadian farmers will lose international competitiveness if Canada rejects the commercialization of GM wheat.

If non-GM wheat is more valuable in the minds of some of the Japanese and UK customers then they should be willing to pay a small non-GM price premium to cover the cost of segregation and to compensate growers for higher unit costs of producing non-GM. Our research leads us to believe that more than 80 percent of the CWB market will purchase GM wheat once it is commercialized in Canada. From a nutritional standpoint it is equivalent to GM wheat and most customers will not see added value in non-GM wheat.

In order to meet potential demand in the UK and Japan for non-GM wheat, segregation of bulk wheat will be required, based on farmer affidavits and overlapping testing. This scheme would be very similar to the ongoing Warburton program, whereby the Canadian industry segregates specific varieties for the UK baker. Segregation of non-GM soybeans in Canada is also successfully meeting the Japanese market conditions for GM free soybeans. The Canadian system has plenty of experience segregating grains and non-GM wheat poses no unusual problems, except for possible low tolerance levels for adventitious presence of GM material. At one time, non-GM and GM canola were segregated but this is no longer the case as there is very little demand for non-GM canola. A similar trend may develop with wheat.

We find that biotech (or GM) wheat would provide prairie grower benefits of about $14 per acre after the technology fee. The percentage gain in net revenue per acre would likely be higher for wheat compared to canola. Many western Canadian wheat growers have experience producing biotech canola and they would quickly adopt GM wheat too. Rich consumers in Japan and the UK can afford to buy non-GM wheat but they may eventually support GM crops if they are made more aware of the environmental benefits.

2. MARKETS FOR CANADIAN HRS WHEAT

As background to our evaluation of the potential marketability of Canadian GM spring wheat, this chapter provides a discussion and analysis of the main characteristics and competitiveness of the world wheat market. We evaluate the likely acceptance of genetically modified (GM) hard red spring wheat in key Canadian markets, and we find the following:

- Canadian wheat growers are more dependent on exports than are US growers.
- Canadian wheat competes mainly in lower quality markets (e.g., the Philippines and Indonesia) that are price sensitive, and substitution among wheat grades and classes is high.
- Future wheat import demand growth is likely to originate from developing countries due to population growth and urbanization.
- There is increasing competition in world wheat markets from non-traditional suppliers such as countries of the Former Soviet Union (FSU).
- Wheat acreage is trending down in western Canada, reflecting a struggling industry and a loss of competitiveness.
- Western Canadian farmers will further lose international competitiveness if the commercialization of GM wheat is rejected in Canada but adopted elsewhere.
- We estimate that approximately 80% of the market for Canadian spring wheat would accept GM wheat, after an initial transition period.

Background: How competitive is the wheat market?
Most Canadian wheat is grown in the prairie provinces of Alberta, Saskatchewan, and Manitoba, under dry land conditions with a very short growing season. The predominant crop is spring wheat (hard red spring and durum) rather than winter wheat, and the dominant class is Canada western red spring (CWRS), planted on more than 75 percent of Canadian wheat acres. CWRS is relatively high in protein "content" and protein "quality" (or strength), ideal for many different types of bread, dough and noodle products eaten around the world, as is the hard red spring (HRS) grown in the United States. In contrast, the dominant wheat class in the United States is hard red winter (HRW). In most markets, there is considerable substitutability among different types of wheat, especially between hard red spring and hard red winter (see Figure 2.1). For instance, in 2002/2003 the reduced availability of HRS led some US millers to substitute HRW for HRS (USDA, Wheat Yearbook, March 2003).

As indicated in Figure 2.1, flour mills in most export markets blend hard red spring wheat with lower protein wheat to increase the gluten content in the flour, and to improve dough handling and water absorption. For instance, in China a flour mill might blend 20 percent CWRS with 80 percent domestic winter wheat to produce bread flour. Alternatively, a U.K. miller might blend 50 percent CWRS with 50 percent domestic British wheat to meet desired flour specifications for bread making.

The Canadian wheat industry is driven by exports to a greater extent than is the US wheat industry. Canada harvests less than 5 percent of the world's wheat crop in any given year, and with its relatively small population, has a large excess supply of wheat to sell onto world markets every year. Normally export sales account for about 70 percent of western Canada's annual wheat production. In comparison, the US depends on export markets for about 50 percent of its wheat production. Apart from exports, about 10 percent of Canadian wheat production is milled for home use, 15 percent is sold domestically as feed, and 5 percent is used locally for seed purposes.

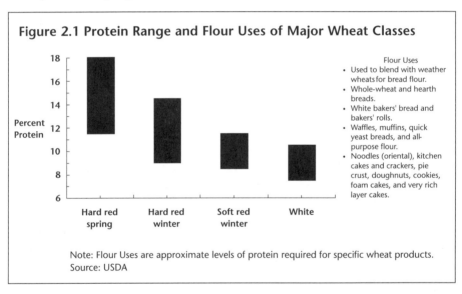

Figure 2.1 Protein Range and Flour Uses of Major Wheat Classes

Flour Uses
- Used to blend with weather wheats for bread flour.
- Whole-wheat and hearth breads.
- White bakers' bread and bakers' rolls.
- Waffles, muffins, quick yeast breads, and all-purpose flour.
- Noodles (oriental), kitchen cakes and crackers, pie crust, doughnuts, cookies, foam cakes, and very rich layer cakes.

Note: Flour Uses are approximate levels of protein required for specific wheat products.
Source: USDA

Despite the fact that prairie wheat growers are dependent on world markets and changes in those markets, including exchange rate fluctuations and shifting import demand, growers are kept in the dark regarding market conditions because their wheat sales are regulated by an agency of the federal government. For instance, the strengthening of the Canadian dollar in

2003 reduced the price of exported wheat in $Cdn by about 80 or 90¢ per bushel, but the prairie grower was not given the opportunity to try and manage that exchange rate risk. Instead it was handled by the CWB.

The Canadian Wheat Board (CWB) is a government state trading enterprise (STE) that has exclusive control over exports of Canadian wheat. The CWB has had an approximate 15 percent market share of world trade in wheat over the past ten years, down from 20 percent in earlier years.[26] The CWB has a poor track record of anticipating market dynamics, as evidenced by the $85.4 million wheat pool deficit in 2002-03.

Over the previous 14 years, CWRS planted acreage on the prairies has been trending down (see Figure 2.2), durum wheat and barley acreage displays no significant trend, and canola acreage has been trending upwards (see Figure 2.3). During the time period shown in Figure 2.2, CWRS prairie acreage reached a maximum of 29.7 million acres in 1992/93. The decline in CWRS acreage reflects a general trend on the Canadian prairies of a movement away from regulated grains due to low profitability and restricted marketing opportunities. Wheat acreage in the Canadian prairies has been shifting to other more profitable crops, and importers are turning away from the CWB to other non-traditional export suppliers. There has been little productivity gain in wheat production on the prairies over the past 10 to 15 years. This point is illustrated by a zero growth rate in prairie wheat yields since 1990.[27]

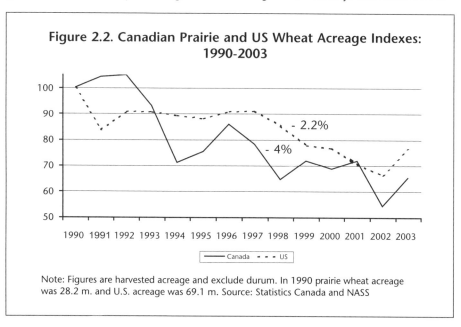

Figure 2.2. Canadian Prairie and US Wheat Acreage Indexes: 1990-2003

Note: Figures are harvested acreage and exclude durum. In 1990 prairie wheat acreage was 28.2 m. and U.S. acreage was 69.1 m. Source: Statistics Canada and NASS

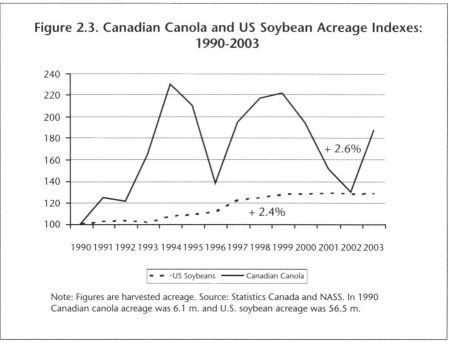

Figure 2.3. Canadian Canola and US Soybean Acreage Indexes: 1990-2003

+ 2.6%

+ 2.4%

1990 1991 1992 1993 1994 1995 1996 1997 1998 1999 2000 2001 2002 2003

- - US Soybeans ——— Canadian Canola

Note: Figures are harvested acreage. Source: Statistics Canada and NASS. In 1990 Canadian canola acreage was 6.1 m. and U.S. soybean acreage was 56.5 m.

In contrast, average canola yields in western Canada have grown by about 1% per year since 1990 (excluding the 2002 harvest).

In the United States, wheat acreage has also fallen quite dramatically–declining by 31 million acres or more than one-third from its peak in 1981, despite significant levels of subsidization. In fact, this decline in US wheat acreage exceeds the entire area devoted to wheat production in Canada. Harvested wheat acreage in Canada (excluding durum) has fallen by about 4% per year, on average, since 1990 (Figure 2.2). During the same time period, US wheat acreage fell by 2.2% per year, on average.[28] The most likely reasons for the decline in US acreage are somewhat different than those behind the fall in Canadian wheat acreage. In the US, decoupled farm program payments (since 1996), relatively better returns from corn and soybeans, and the idling of land through the conservation reserve program, have all contributed to a shift of acreage out of wheat. As in Canada, there has been minimal productivity gain in US wheat production compared to corn and soybeans where biotechnology has been rapidly adopted.

For some time, the CWB has claimed that its customers can be segregated from each other and then charged different prices for the same wheat (Kraft, Furtan, and Tyrchniewicz). As a result, the CWB and several economists assert that the CWB is able to price discriminate among different countries, charging higher prices for sales of a given quality of wheat in some countries and lower prices in others. This requires restricting export volumes and segmenting markets. Kraft, Furtan, and Tyrchniewicz concluded that the CWB's price discrimination policies increased prices received by the CWB by C$13 to C$27 per metric ton, on average. We believe this figure is highly exaggerated and any price premiums received in foreign markets for Canadian wheat are payments for quality attributes, not premiums obtained through the exercise of market power.

Our research has found that world wheat markets are highly competitive (that is, elasticities of import demand for wheat are quite large for most importers), and therefore market power is not a defensible rationale for single desk selling. Recently, Furtan, Gray and Holzman (2003b) (p. 437) suggested that the CWB is a price taker in world markets, in concurrence with our view of the world wheat market today. In foreign markets for milling wheat (such as Japan, Indonesia, Iran, China, and Brazil) Canada faces significant competition from other suppliers. However the 1996 Kraft, Furtan, and Tyrchniewicz study singled out Brazil as an imperfectly competitive market. Furthermore, it was estimated by Kraft, Furtan, and Tyrchniewicz that in the Brazilian market "CWB sales have occurred at substantially higher prices than other competitors in the market" (p.111). Most of the CWB sales to Brazil reportedly involved relatively high quality hard red spring wheat. Kuntz (2001) also identified Brazil as one of ten key markets "at-risk" as a lost export market for Canada from the introduction of GM wheat.

Figure 2.4 displays the CWB's annual share of Brazilian wheat imports, illustrating that this market is much more competitive than previously described by the CWB. During the 1990s and into the current decade, the CWB's share of Brazil's imports fell from about one-third to essentially zero, yet Brazil remains one of the world's largest wheat importers, purchasing around 6 to 7 mmt per year. Argentina now meets most of the Brazilian wheat import demand, with the US and countries of the former Soviet Union (FSU)–including the Ukraine and Kazakhstan–making some inroads into this market. Canada's annual exports to Brazil have averaged less than 100,000 mt over the last four years. Interestingly, Brazil emerged as a temporary wheat exporter in 2003/04, exporting about 400,000 mt, and illustrating the flexibility and competitiveness of the international wheat market.[29]

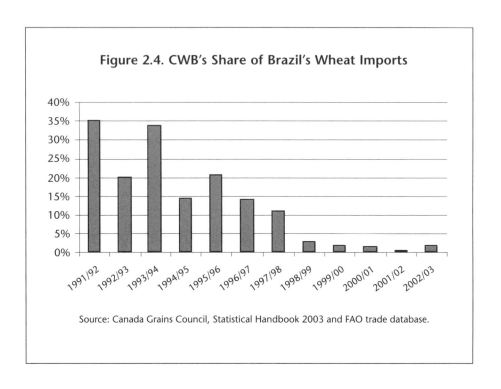

Figure 2.4. CWB's Share of Brazil's Wheat Imports

Source: Canada Grains Council, Statistical Handbook 2003 and FAO trade database.

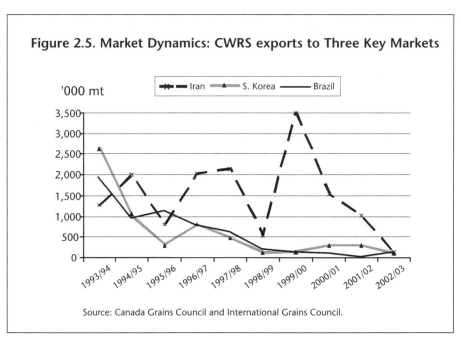

Figure 2.5. Market Dynamics: CWRS exports to Three Key Markets

Source: Canada Grains Council and International Grains Council.

Other important overseas markets for CWRS have eroded, contradicting the CWB claim that major importers cannot easily substitute away from Canadian wheat. Ten years ago, Brazil, Iran and S. Korea combined accounted for over 30 percent of CWB wheat exports. In the past few years, these three importers have almost completely substituted away from CWRS imports (see Figure 2.5). As the Australian Productivity Commission has observed, gains from price discrimination by export STEs like the CWB are unlikely to be large.

In the Middle East, it is not just Iran that has reduced its total wheat imports. Overall, Middle Eastern wheat imports have been nearly halved over the last five years, to less than 10 mmt, as domestic production has expanded.[30] Australia has traditionally been a very large exporter of wheat to this region and so this shift in trade will force Australia to find new markets, creating greater competition for Canada and other exporters.

World Wheat Production and Consumption
Production
World wheat production in the past three or four years has been just under 600 mmt, which is below the long-term trend. Global wheat production is concentrated in a relatively small number of countries, but the number of major producers has grown recently. The European Union (EU), China, India, the United States, Russia, Canada, Australia, Pakistan, Turkey, the Ukraine, Argentina, and Kazakhstan account for over 80 percent of the world wheat production. The EU is the world's leading wheat producer, followed by China, India, and the United States. Canada is a relatively small player on the production side.

The total volume of world wheat production has approximately doubled in the past three decades. The annual production growth rate averaged 2.06 percent during the 1970 to 2000 time period (see Table 2.1). Most of the growth in wheat production came from increased yields, rather than increased acreage. From 1970 to 2000, yields grew 2.04 percent per year on average, and the area growth rate was essentially zero, on average (see Table 2.1). But there was variation in the acreage growth rate during the period. The wheat area harvested grew in the 1970s at about 1.22 percent per year, and then turned negative in the 1980s and 1990s.

Increases in world wheat yields were significant in the 1970s and 1980s, but average yield growth slowed considerably in the 1990s. In the 1970s, yields grew at over 2 percent per year and they rose even faster in the 1980s, at about 2.75 percent per year, on average. In the 1990s the average annual yield growth rate was 0.8 percent per year worldwide. In all of Canada, wheat yields grew an average of 0.9 percent per year during the same time period.

Even though wheat yields in the United States grew at 1.3 percent a year in the 1990s, they did not grow as fast as US corn and soybean yields during this same period. One reason for this difference is that the pace of genetic improvement for wheat has been slower than for competing crops for a number of reasons, including technical breeding issues. However, it is also the case that seed companies have been discouraged from investing in wheat research due to lower potential returns, compared to corn or soybeans (Vocke).

Table 2.1. Growth Rates in World Wheat Production, Consumption, and Trade: 1970-2000 (Average Annual Percentage Change)

	Area	Yield	Production	Consumption	Trade
1970s	1.22	2.07	3.29	2.78	3.98
1980s	-0.92	2.75	1.82	2.3	0.75*
1990s	-0.17*	0.82	0.65*	0.8	-0.51*
1970-2000	0.02*	2.04	2.06	2.09	2.09

Note: * denotes coefficients insignificant at the 10% level. Original Data Source: Wheat Yearbook by ERS, USDA (http://usda.mannlib.cornell.edu/). The growth rates are estimated by the following regression: ln (y) = a + b * time.

The FSU experienced a steep drop in the average growth of wheat yields in the 1990s. In this region, the average annual growth in yields fell from +3 percent in the 1980s to –3 percent in the 1990s, a huge swing. Lower subsidies, problems with input procurement, and inefficient markets, all contributed to the severe fall in the growth of wheat yields in the FSU.

Consumption
Wheat is the primary grain consumed by humans around the globe. About 75 percent of the world's wheat is consumed directly, and another 15 percent indirectly in the form of animal products. This leaves 10 percent for seed and industrial use. The global consumption of wheat has doubled in the last thirty years to reach approximately 600 mmt per year. Consumption expanded by an average of about 5.6 mmt per year in the last decade, due to rising population and incomes, and due to increased urbanization with its associated changing dietary patterns. Future growth

in wheat consumption is expected to originate mainly from developing countries, the same source that accounted for recent growth in global wheat consumption. According to United Nations data, in developing countries the population is growing by about 1.4 percent per year, compared to almost zero growth, on average, in developed countries.[31] In addition, urbanization is a phenomenon that is largely confined to the developing world.

Feed use accounts for a relatively small share of total world wheat consumption. During the last decade, this share has dropped from approximately 20 percent of global use to just 15 percent. The main explanation for this shift in feed use was a dramatic decline in use of wheat for feed in the former Soviet Union (FSU).

Outside the FSU, regional patterns of feed use of wheat vary dramatically from region to region. For instance, average feed consumption of wheat is relatively high in the European Union (EU) and Canada, around 45 to 50 percent of total domestic consumption (or about 15% of total production). Alternatively, feed consumption of wheat is relatively low in the United States (around 15 percent of domestic use).

Wheat Trade

Like production, global trade in wheat in recent years is below the long-term trend. However, in absolute volume, the international wheat trade remains larger than for any other single grain, averaging about 105 mmt over the last decade–or almost 20 percent of total world production. The trade is primarily from the north to the south, as developed countries now account for about 85 percent of the wheat exports and the developing countries account for about 75 percent of the import volume.

The world markets for wheat can be viewed as consisting of markets for two distinct commodities – milling wheat and durum wheat. The world milling wheat export market is relatively large, involving an annual average of approximately 95 mmt in total world exports in the 1990s, and can be further segmented into two broad categories. The first is a small high quality and high–priced market (including countries such as Japan and the United Kingdom) that demands precise specifications with regard to protein, hardness, moisture, color, etc. The second is a large lower quality and lower priced market (including countries such as Indonesia, China, Iran, and Egypt) in which specifications are very loose. Several studies have pointed out that Canada has missed market opportunities and given up revenue by focusing on high quality wheat and not adequately diversifying into medium and lower quality wheat.[32]

Referring to Figure 2.6, it is evident that growth in global wheat trade has been relatively small since the end of the 1970s. Trade grew rapidly during the 1970s and then leveled off during the early 1980s and throughout the 1990s. From Table 2.1, we see that, on average, trade grew by almost 4 percent per year in the 1970s, growing faster than production (3.29 percent). The average growth rate in world wheat trade slowed to 0.75 percent per year in the 1980s and then became negative in the 1990s.

The United States has traditionally been the largest wheat exporter, followed by the EU, Canada, Australia, and Argentina. Recently, a number of new exporters have emerged that are of consequence in aggregate. These exporters include Russia, the Ukraine, Kazakhstan, India, and Hungary. In particular, exports from countries of the Former Soviet Union–Ukraine, Russia, and Kazakhstan–have surged to the point where their export volume reached 25.8 mmt in 2002/03, making this region the world's largest exporter ahead of the United States in that year.[33] Canadian HRS wheat is extremely vulnerable to competition from these emerging exporters.

Kazakhstan is the most important producer of high-protein wheat in Asia and Europe (Longmire and Moldashev) and is emerging as a low cost major competitor of Canada's in some traditional offshore markets. Following independence in the early 1990s, Kazakhstan's planted wheat area plunged to less than one-half of its peak of over 44.5 million acres

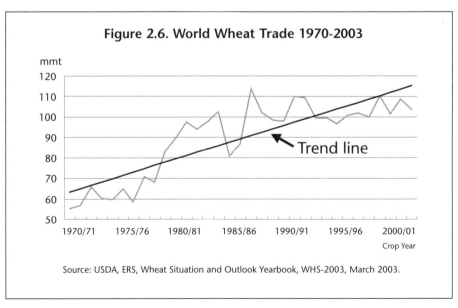

Figure 2.6. World Wheat Trade 1970-2003

Source: USDA, ERS, Wheat Situation and Outlook Yearbook, WHS-2003, March 2003.

(see Figure 2.7). In 2002/03 sown area recovered somewhat to 28.4 million acres and this country produced 12.6 mmt of wheat.[34] But there is considerable room for further recovery of wheat production in this central Asian country. Kazakhstan is developing new port facilities on the Caspian Sea, which will greatly facilitate exports to Iran and other parts of the Middle East. In addition, Kazakhstan will be a strong competitor in Africa and Asia.

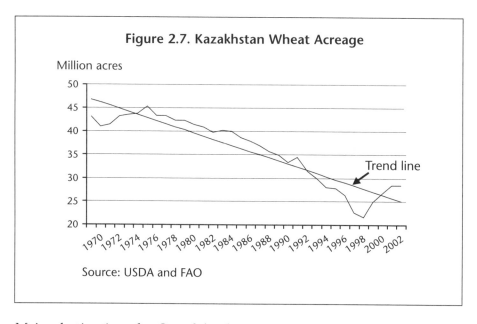

Figure 2.7. Kazakhstan Wheat Acreage

Million acres

Trend line

Source: USDA and FAO

Major destinations for Canada's wheat exports are reported in Table 2.2. This table shows that Canada is highly dependent on low to middle income countries in the case of spring wheat sales (e.g., China, Iran and Indonesia). These countries are relatively poor and therefore, we believe, willing to trade off wheat quality for price. Additional insights into individual importing countries of importance to Canada are provided below.

Import demand for wheat in East Asia, Latin America, and North Africa (all developing regions) has continued to grow. That is the reason that global wheat trade has not fallen dramatically with the departure of China and the FSU from the import market. China and the former Soviet Union together were large wheat importers during the early 1980s, at one point accounting for one-third of total world imports. However, their combined significance as importers declined sharply in the 1990s. The strong possibility that developing countries will account for most of the import demand growth in the foreseeable future is extremely important for exporters, because developing countries tend to import lower quality wheat. The east-Asian market (excluding China) is now the largest importing region and imports by this region have doubled in the last decade. In South America, Argentina and Brazil are major players in the wheat market and ongoing policy and infrastructure developments in these two countries have the potential to change the shape of the international market. Both Argentina and Brazil have tremendous untapped potential to expand grain and oilseed production (Schnepf and Dohlman). Argentina is one of the top five exporters. Its wheat production increased by nearly 50 percent in the 1990s and there remains good potential for additional growth in wheat production. Recent gains in production have been driven by area expansion and dramatic increases in yields, due to improved varieties and more intensive use of inputs. Future growth is expected to manifest itself more in the form of higher yields, as opposed to area expansion (Wainio and Raney).

Table 2.2. Major Canadian Wheat Markets: CWRS 1997/98-2001/02 Average

	CWRS Import Volume (mmt)	Share of CWRS exports	Main CWRS Competitors
Iran	1,631	14.0%	Argentina, Australia, FSU, Domestic
Japan	1,269	10.9%	Australia, US
United States	1,017	8.7%	Domestic
Mexico	730	6.3%	US, Domestic
Indonesia	622	5.3%	Australia, EU, US
China	581	5.0%	Australia, US, Domestic
Philippines	491	4.2%	Australia, US
Colombia	473	4.1%	US
Venezuela	448	3.8%	US
United Kingdom	356	3.1%	US, EU, Domestic
Guatemala	305	2.6%	US
Peru	302	2.6%	Argentina, US

Source: compiled from Canada Grains Council, Statistical Handbook, 2003. Main competitors are authors' estimates.

In contrast to Argentina, Brazil is one of the largest wheat importers in the world. However, Brazil's dependence on imports could change in the coming years due to significant new investment in infrastructure (Ekboir). At the present time, high transportation costs discourage grain production in the central part of Brazil, but the Brazilian government recently announced plans to develop a north-south water transportation corridor that will allow the development of agricultural production in the *Cerrado* savanna region (in the center of the country). The higher altitude in the *Cerrado* region is more conducive to wheat production. In addition, because wheat is available as a winter crop, its production should increase with the growing popularity of zero tillage and the agronomic benefits of including wheat in a crop rotation that also includes soybeans and maize. Iran was the major foreign market for CWRS during the period reported in Table 2.2, however as mentioned above, Iran's imports have dropped off in the past few years. Japan, the United States, and the United Kingdom accounted for a total of about 23 percent of CWRS exports during the five year period summarized in Table 2.2.

Some portion of the Japanese, US, and U.K. markets would most likely be willing to pay a price premium for non-GM wheat, but the other markets shown in Table 2.2 likely would not.

Although Canada produces very high quality wheat, the vast majority of the world wheat trade is standard quality. Table 2.3 shows the world trade in high quality wheat for the period 1992–1996. During this time period, there were only three exporters of "high-quality" wheat: Canada, Australia, and the United States. Canadian wheat had a large share (39%) of the high quality wheat market, but less than the US share (51%). Importantly, high quality wheat is a very small part (about 8%) of the overall world wheat trade. The rest of world trade is standard quality wheat, including feed wheat. Canada's high quality wheat cannot command a quality premium in the "standard" quality market.

Table 2.3. Common Wheat Quality Groups (1992 – 1996)

	World Trade (mmt)	% of High Quality
High Quality		
1 & 2 CWRS ≥ 13%	3.3	39%
HRS ≥ 14%	4.24	51%
Aus. Prime Hard	0.87	10%
sum	8.4 (8%)	
Standard Quality (incl. feed)	92.2	

Source: Manitoba Rural Adaptation Council and CWB, 1999.

Reserve Stocks and Prices

Measured in real terms, international wheat prices have trended downward for many years, reflecting the fact that world wheat supply has kept pace with demand (Antle and Smith). The most recent upward deviation from this trend in prices occurred with a short-lived spike in world wheat prices in early 1996, when the average price of wheat in May was US$260 per mt. However, weak import demand and increased stocks-to-use levels after 1996 resulted in a sudden collapse of wheat prices and a reversion to the long-term downward trend in real prices, with only temporary price reversals.

Over the past ten years, global wheat "end-of-year" stocks have averaged about 184 mmt, or 28 percent of annual consumption. This level of carryover stocks is consistent with the long-term average over the past 30-40 years (Carter, Revoredo and Smith) even though the US and EU governments have reduced stock holdings from levels attained in the mid 1980s.

One of the most important variables in the world wheat equation, the size of China's grain reserves, is a state secret. This is an important factor because China may hold as much as one-third of the world's wheat reserves. In 2001, both the FAO and the USDA suddenly revised their previous estimates of China's domestic stocks of wheat, rice, and corn. The abrupt fall in China's grain production in 2000 did not lead to large imports, as expected, and partly for this reason, the FAO and USDA decided that China must have been sitting on large stockpiles of grain.[35]

The US Department of Agriculture (USDA) increased its estimate of China's 2000/2001 ending grain stocks from 66.1 million metric tons (mmt) to 230.1 mmt–more than a tripling of the figure. The USDA's stock figure for wheat was revised from 13.7 to 54.2 mmt, a quadrupling of the estimate. A few months earlier the FAO had revised its total cereal grain stock estimate for China from 28.1 mmt to 364 mmt–nearly 13 times more than its previous estimate. The FAO's revisions for China were so large that it meant more than a doubling of its estimate of the amount of world cereal grain reserves to 640 mmt at the end of crop year 2001.

As shown in Figure 2.8, there has been a dramatic shift in terms of which countries hold wheat stock reserves. Prior to the mid 1990s the major exporters held around 30% of the global wheat reserves. As the United States and the EU have purposefully reduced stockholding, the share of reserves held by the major exporters declined to less than 20%. At the same time, the share held by China and India expanded to more than 50% of world reserves.

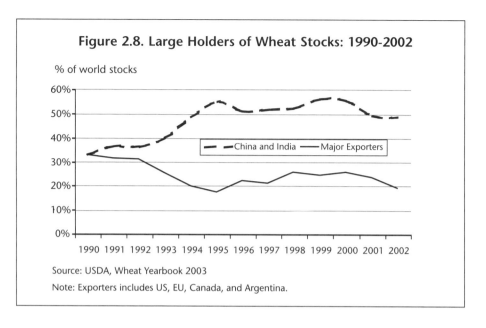

Figure 2.8. Large Holders of Wheat Stocks: 1990-2002

% of world stocks

China and India — Major Exporters

Source: USDA, Wheat Yearbook 2003

Note: Exporters includes US, EU, Canada, and Argentina.

This change in stockholding has some interesting implications. First, the two most populous countries in the world now hold the majority of wheat stocks. China and India, combined, account for over one-third of the world's population. Second, the quality of the wheat held in storage by China and India is probably inferior to the wheat that was previously held by the US and the EU. Third, China and India's stocks will serve primarily as reserves to smooth supply shocks within each of those countries, rather than to offset supply shocks elsewhere in the world. Fourth, a large share of the stocks in China and India may be privately held, whereas the US and the EU governments were previously large stockholders. Small private stockholders will respond differently to market shocks, compared to large government stockholding corporations. As a result of this interesting development in global wheat reserves, world wheat prices may now be more sensitive to supply shocks outside of India and China.

Key Import Markets for CWRS
United Kingdom

The U.K. has long-standing links with Canada through its pre-EU membership system of Commonwealth preferences and its special trade relations during and before World War II. The U.K. was a large importer of spring wheat from North America until the formation of the EU in the late 1950s. From the 1960s through the 1990s, wheat prices in the U.K. were well above world levels, but they are now close to world prices due to EU agricultural policy reform.

The U.K. industry mills about 5.6 mmt of wheat per year, 84% of which is purchased from domestic growers. Approximately 5% is purchased from other EU countries and a total of 11% is imported from non-EU countries, such as Canada, the United States, Australia, and the Ukraine. In a typical year, the U.K. imports about 300,000 mt of wheat from Canada, about 5% of total U.K. usage. Small amounts of Australian, Canadian and Ukrainian organic wheat enter the U.K. for milling purposes, often via containers. There is considerable flexibility in the milling and baking process in the U.K. This means that through blending different wheat and by adding gluten, the U.K. mills can use various combinations of U.K., other European, or North American wheat to produce flour of desired quality.

Approximately one-half of current U.K. wheat imports from Canada are through the Warburton program, whereby the Warburton bakery in the U.K. contracts with Canadian growers through agents in Canada. This program involves three different wheat varieties and segregates the contracted wheat through the handling and storage system. Warburton's bread is made up of about 50% CWRS and 50% domestically sourced wheat.

In the U.K. market, the substitutability between Dark Northern Spring from the United States and CWRS from Canada has been increasing in the recent past, largely due to the introduction of new US varieties and improved responsiveness of the US system to U.K. miller needs. As a result, two of the largest U.K. millers and bakers recently moved away from purchases of CWRS towards purchases of DNS. The US now exports more hard red spring to the EU than does Canada. In the UK, the price spread between CWRS and DNS is approximately $5 to $7/mt ($US), with CWRS trading at a premium.

The U.K. milling industry is highly concentrated. The four-firm concentration ratio is about 75% or higher. In 1998 the Monopolies Commission reviewed the industry and disallowed Rank Hovis' proposed purchase of 4 additional mills.[36] The average U.K. wheat mill is relatively large by European standards but relatively small by North American standards. In the U.K., mills produce almost 66,000 mt of flour per year, on average. There are a total of about 68 flour mills in the U.K.[37] Most milling companies are integrated into the baking side of the industry. For example, Rank Hovis and Allied (the two largest millers with 25 to 30% of the market each) have their own bakeries. Baking may be even more concentrated than milling.

There are four large food retailers in the U.K. that account for about 70% of bread sales. All supermarkets account for 90% of retail bread sales. The four large companies are Tesco, Sainsbury's, Safeway, and ASDA (part of Wal-Mart). At the retail level, bread is relatively inexpensive in the U.K., and the U.K. bread market is split into four sub-markets. These categories are (from least to most expensive) value, standard, premium, and super premium. The UK price range for off-the-shelf bread is wider than the price range in most North American markets. The implications of this wide price range are that the cheap bread serves as a loss leader for the retailer and the higher priced super premium bread reflects the value of baker brand names (e.g., Warburton) arising from high advertising expenses and relatively high packaging costs.

The higher priced super premium "brand named" breads typically use some spring wheat imported from North America. The ratio of North American wheat in super premium bread runs from zero to 70%. There is little or no North American imported wheat in the cheap UK breads. Some of the higher priced bread uses US DNS and some uses Canadian CWRS. Approximately five years ago there was a switch towards DNS and away from CWRS.

It is becoming very common for U.K. millers to buy domestic and EU wheat by variety, requiring a variety declaration on every shipment. For some of the cheaper wheat (say from Germany) the U.K. mills might buy "groups" of varieties in a single shipment.

In 1994, Warburton bakeries approached the CWB with a request to procure CWRS by variety. They were originally interested in three varieties (Teal, Columbus, and Pasqua). Baking problems arising from a shift in varieties grown on the Canadian prairies in the late 1980s prompted this request from Warburton. In particular, the widespread adoption of Roblin, Katepwa, and Laura varieties in Canada created baking problems for Warburton. Although the varieties available then were within the "equal to Neepawa" range, they produced somewhat different baking characteristics. The varieties now selected are Barrie, Elsa and Teal.

The Warburton program is an established segregation program that works very successfully in the Canadian bulk handling system and creates added value. It works so well because there are financial incentives for the growers and handlers. Furthermore, there is a tight monitoring system in place. Like malting barley, the unselected product of over-booked acres has an alternative market. And the segregation is accomplished successfully within a bulk handling system.

What do we learn from the Warburton program? First, it serves as a possible model of a segregation system for non-GM wheat.[38] Second, in more specialized markets like the U.K. market, there is a movement towards more specialized demand. In contrast, the Canadian grain system aggregates many of the relevant product characteristics and cannot accomplish specialized segregation.

The current Canadian wheat grading system requires that all varieties in a given class be visually indistinguishable from one another and visually distinguishable from wheat belonging to a different class. This system is awkward for many end users who could create value through procurement of single varieties, but are prevented from doing so in the current system. They can only purchase a class of wheat that is made up of different varieties. Instead of the current Canadian system, varietal characteristics and varietal acquisition is what is required in today's marketplace. In a few years, this may not even be sufficient. For example, Warburton actually goes beyond varietal segregation and now selects by region and by producer in western Canada.

In 2003, the Canadian Grain Commission (CGC) considered and then rejected the introduction of a new system intended to better identify and track grain by variety, the variety eligibility declaration (VED) system.[39] The VED system would have replaced the existing kernel visual distinguishability (KVD) system. However, in the end the CGC determined that the benefits of a mandatory VED system would not outweigh the costs. This keeps the Canadian grain handling system well behind developments in the rest of the world where wheat is increasingly bought and sold based on variety.

Japan

Japan's Food Agency (FA), a state trader, controls Japan's wheat imports. The FA imports wheat from three export sources: Australia, Canada, and the United States. The exporter market shares are relatively constant from year-to-year, as follows: United States 54%, Canada 26%, and Australia, 20%. All FA imports are procured through weekly tenders and there are 29 Japanese trading houses that are licensed to tender offers to the FA.

The FA makes a significant profit on wheat imports (about $1.2 billion USD per year) because it re-sells wheat imports to domestic users at more than double the (cif) world price. Approximately 40% of this wheat profit is used by the FA to subsidize domestic wheat production through high farm gate prices. FA earns an estimated profit of about $3.6 million (USD) per 20,000 mt. vessel of wheat imports. So the FA can clearly afford to pay for segregation costs if it decides to import some non-GM wheat after GM wheat is commercialized.

From Canada, the FA imports primarily No. 1 CWRS (13.5% protein), plus some durum. More than 80% of imported Canadian wheat is used for producing bread in Japan. About 15% of the CWRS is used for blending with softer wheat for noodles. The remaining 5% is used for soya sauce or bread crumbs. In Japan, consumers eat about 100 kg. of starch per year; about one-third of this consumption is wheat and two-thirds is rice.

For many years, the Canadian Wheat Board has maintained a long-term agreement with the FA, but this agreement was not renewed in 2002. With regard to wheat imports, the FA appears to be shifting from quality concerns to cost concerns. CWRS exports to Japan compete with DNS from the United States and a small volume of Prime Hard from Australia. Relative to DNS, the reported price premium paid by the FA for CWRS is approximately $5 per mt (USD).

The FA imports a relatively small amount of feed wheat every year (about 100,000 mt). Feed wheat imports are conducted under a separate program from food wheat. Feed wheat imports are channeled through a simultaneous buy-sell (SBS) system, similar to that for rice. Under the SBS system, designated buyers and accredited importers work together to put together a bid (with a price spread) to the FA. The FA chooses the bid with the most favorable price spread.

The wheat milling industry in Japan contends that Japanese consumers are reluctant to purchase food products containing GM ingredients. There are hardly any food products available in Japanese retail food stores that are labeled as containing GM material, but this does not mean that Japanese consumers are not eating GM foods. Instead, it means the GM food labeling regulations are flexible.

Japanese GM food labeling regulations were introduced in 2001 (USDA, FAS, Feb. 2003). The labeling regulations apply to a list of 24 food products. If the food is not on the list, there is no labeling requirement. For example, beer and canola oil are not on the list. For those products on the list, the regulations apply to the top 3 ingredients by weight of final product. If one of the top 3 ingredients has more than 5% GM material, then the food product must be labeled as GM.

The major farm organization in Japan is JA Zenchu (a central union of agricultural cooperatives). This cooperative is organized throughout the country, with the purpose of protecting farming. It is engaged in various activities including the marketing of farm products and inputs. Almost every farmer in Japan is a member of the local branch of the cooperative. JA Zenchu has not formally opposed GM foods.[40]

If GM wheat is commercially produced in North America and purchased by Japan, wheat products sold in Japan would have to be labeled; the only question is the tolerance level. The Ministry of Agriculture Fisheries and Forestry (MAFF) administers the labeling.[41]

Food processors and retailers in Japan have found there is little premium for non-GM food products. For example, non-GM soya sauce is labeled as such but does not sell well compared to GM soya sauce. Most snack foods are promoted as non-GM, through voluntary labeling.

Japan's wheat imports are tested for pesticide residue at three stages. The first stage is at the point of loading the vessel. The second stage is done in Japan with samples that are shipped ahead of the vessel. The third stage is testing during the unloading of the vessel.

The residue testing is conducted for more than 100 different pesticide chemicals. The residue testing procedure is important because there is already extensive testing and pre-clearance of the sort that would be required under a segregation system for GM wheat. The residue tolerance levels conform to WHO standards. The cost of the first stage of the test in Canada conducted by the Canadian Grain Commission is $8,000 (CDN) per vessel (typically for a 20,000 mt vessel). If there are two separate classes of wheat on the same vessel then the cost is $16,000 per vessel. A Japanese firm (OMIC) is starting to do these tests in Vancouver for 373,000 Yen (about one-half the cost of the CGC test). This ongoing testing practice would facilitate the type of testing that would be required by Japan for non-GM wheat.

The wheat milling industry in Japan is more concentrated than is the baking industry. The top two wheat mills (Nisshin and Nippon) account for about 60% of production and the top four mills account for about 80% (Showa and Nitto are in the top four). The largest baker (Yamazaki) in Japan has about 25 to 30% of the bread market. There are several national bakeries with 5 to 6% of the market each. Some of these bakeries have regional strength. Food retailing in Japan has undergone significant changes recently. The largest food retailers in Japan are now the 7-Eleven convenience stores, owned by Ito-Yokado. Baked goods are prominently displayed in food stores and emphasis is placed on the freshness of baked goods. Large-scale retailers like Wal-Mart and Costco are beginning to make inroads into the Japanese market.

In a press release, the Japanese Millers Association stated that there are significant technical issues associated with implementing a segregation system for GM wheat. The Millers Association has indicated that every wheat shipment would have to be tested for GM content and the costs would be too high. However, with GM wheat there would be less need for the extensive pesticide residue testing that is now routinely done by Japanese importers, because GM wheat would be produced with fewer chemicals. In any case, the costs of testing are rather inexpensive.

The data indicate that Japan is highly dependent on Canada and the United States as a source of supply of hard spring wheat. The Japanese millers suggest they would switch to alternative sources if GM wheat were to be licensed in Canada and the United States. However, Australia or other exporters could not supply the volume and type of wheat demanded by Japan. Instead, Japan would have to source supplies from the FSU. Of course, this would open up other markets to Canada and the US

The Tokyo Grain Exchange trades futures contracts for both GM soybeans and non-GM soybeans. Non-GM soybeans trade at a premium over GM soybeans, but this spread has declined over time and is presently about $12/mt.

Each year Japan imports close to 5 mmt of soybeans, of which approximately 1 mmt are non-GM. The non-GM soybeans are imported from the United States (450,000 mt), Canada (300,000 mt), China (130,000 mt), and small amounts from Australia and Brazil. These imported soybeans are handled with a relatively low cost and well established segregation system that has been in operation for many years. Tofu processors in Japan want specific varieties of soybeans and that is why a segregation system was in place even before GM soybean production took hold in the United States and elsewhere.

Indonesia
With 220 million people, Indonesia is one of the most heavily populated countries in the world. It is also one of the largest importers of wheat because there is no domestic production due to its tropical climate.

Recently, Indonesia has imported about 4.8 mmt of wheat per year (including approximately 290,000 mt of flour). The exact volume of flour imports is uncertain due to extensive smuggling to avoid the Indonesian VAT and sales tax.

Australia accounts for the largest market share in the Indonesian wheat market, with 60% of the market in 2001/02. In that same year, Canada, the United States, and India supplied 11%, 7%, and 6% respectively.[42] Smaller suppliers of wheat to Indonesia include France and Argentina. In 2001/02, flour imports originated from India, China, the United Arab Emirates, and Australia.

Most US wheat sold into Indonesia is soft wheat, with small amounts of DNS. Canada sells primarily CWRS No. 1 and 2 and the CWRS is blended with soft wheat from Australia and the United States for noodle flour, bread flour, and biscuit and cake flour. Approximately 50% of the Indonesian flour is produced for (wet and dry) noodles, 25% for cakes and baked goods, 15% for biscuits, 5% for household use and 5% for fried foods.[43]

Australia's relatively large market share in the Indonesian market is due to its proximity and Indonesia's historical preference for dealing with the Australian Wheat Board. Australia enjoys a freight advantage of $7 to $10 per mt. relative to the US Pacific Northwest or Vancouver. In addition, the time on the high seas is almost two weeks shorter from Australia compared to the PNW or Vancouver. The timing is critical for wheat mills in Indonesia that are exposed to significant exchange rate risk, especially since the Asian financial crisis in the late 1990s.

The Indonesian mills import wheat directly and there is no import tariff. However, a small amount of protection is afforded the mills as flour imports are assessed a 5% tariff. Both wheat and flour imports are subject to a 10% VAT tax and a 2.5% sales tax.

For many years, Indonesia's state trader (BULOG) controlled wheat imports. However, the wheat market was liberalized in 1998 due to pressure from the International Monetary Fund during the Asian financial crisis. During the BULOG period of monopoly control, there was only one Indonesian wheat milling company (Bogasari), which was essentially milling for the government and simply collecting a fee on each mt milled.

The Indonesian wheat market was not focused on quality during the BULOG period. BULOG purchased the imported wheat and sold the flour, so Bogasari had little or no say regarding the quality of imports. Now that the market is liberalized, demand for wheat products is gradually becoming more sophisticated and more attention is paid to high protein wheat. Previously the mills produced three types of flour: high protein (>12%), medium protein (10 to 11%), and low protein (8 to 9%). Since deregulation the mills have expanded product lines and now produce 6 to 8 different flour categories.

The milling industry is highly concentrated as one firm (Bogasari) accounts for more than 70% of domestic flour production. Bogasari has four plants and is reportedly the largest flour miller in the world. There are three smaller firms, Berdikari (9%), Sriboga (5%), and Panganmas (5%).

With the removal of BULOG's wheat monopoly, flour imports started to increase to the point where they now account for about 8 to 10% of consumption. The domestic mills are therefore running below capacity. In 2001, the Indonesian wheat mills filed a flour anti-dumping complaint against the European Union, Australia, and the United Arab Emirates. The Indonesian government found that dumping was occurring and duties were imposed in 2003 and 2004.

Indonesia has approved the planting of GM cotton and researchers in Indonesia are working on a large number of crops. These include rice, corn, cotton, peanuts, cacao, soybeans, sugarcane, tobacco, sweet potato, and potatoes. The Indonesian government has introduced mandatory food labeling for GM food products but the regulations have not yet been implemented. The labeling regulations apply to both raw materials and processed food products. For processed food, the labeling regulations apply to packaged food products only. This distinction is important because a high ratio of the meals consumed in Indonesia are purchased from street vendors. For example, wet noodles are the largest market for flour in Indonesia and these noodles are sold primarily through street vendors. Only a small share of the noodles is purchased in packages. Indonesia's labeling laws will have little or no impact on wheat because the significant majority of the consumers will never see the results of the regulations. They do not buy packaged wheat products.

The Indonesian wheat mills would have no need to buy non-GM wheat. Indonesian consumers are very price conscious and would not be willing to pay any premium for non-GM flour. The growth in cheap imported flour and the problem with smuggled flour imports underscores the fact that consumers pay attention to price. There is little or no price difference between CWRS and DNS wheat purchases by the Indonesian mills. In fact, most CWRS destined for Indonesia is purchased through Japanese multinational trading houses.

China

China is the largest producer and consumer of wheat in the world (excluding the enlarged EU). Production was 86 mmt in 2003, 95% of which was winter wheat acreage. Wheat production in the last few years is down about 20% from levels attained in the 1990s, due to a reduction in planted acreage in response to government policy change and the elimination of government procurement at protected prices.[44]

Recently, China's government has taken steps to encourage the production of "higher" quality wheat, whereas the previous focus was on quantity rather than quality. Spring wheat acreage has dropped more than winter wheat, on a percentage basis. Spring wheat acreage has fallen by about 40% in the last few years. The government has dropped the support price for spring wheat and now the support price applies to winter wheat. In China, domestic spring wheat is considered to be inferior to domestic winter wheat.

China's total domestic wheat consumption in 2003 was estimated (by the USDA FAS) to be 105 mmt, which is almost entirely used for human consumption. Only a small amount of wheat is used for animal feed in China (about 6 mmt). Traditionally, wheat flour in China is used for Chinese noodles, dumplings and steamed breads. These uses account for over 90% of wheat flour usage. Cakes, cookies and breads are becoming more popular in China, but still account for a relatively small share of the wheat flour market.

China National Cereals Oils and Foodstuffs Import and Export Corporation (COFCO), a large state-trading agency, historically has controlled China's wheat trade. COFCO is one of the largest trading companies in China and is listed as one of the Global Top 500 Enterprises by Fortune magazine. COFCO is involved in commodity trade (especially grains and oils exports and imports), food processing, real estate, life insurance, etc. China's WTO entry will place competitive pressure on COFCO.

In theory, COFCO imports wheat for either the market (i.e., domestic millers) or for the state grain reserve (SAGR). In recent years, all imports have been for the reserve. For example, the "special" 400,000 mt purchase from Canada in 2000 went into the government reserve and most of that wheat remains in storage. COFCO reportedly pays $4 to $5 per mt. more for CWRS than for US DNS with the same protein level. One reason that COFCO is willing to pay slightly more for CWRS is that it is cleaner and more consistent than DNS and quite often the CWB over-delivers on both the grade and protein level. Until recently, China would not import wheat from Portland (due to TCK smut concerns) and this favored CWRS over DNS.

COFCO earns a 1% commission on wheat exports and imports and it incurs none of the price risk or exchange rate risk typically associated with commodity importing or exporting. This risk is borne entirely by COFCO's domestic clients, mostly the state agencies that either store or process grain.

Recently, China temporarily reverted to a net exporter of wheat. Imports (exports) in 2000/01 were 446,000 mt (470,000 mt), in 2001/02 572,000 mt (651,000 mt), and in 2002/03 425,000 mt (1,718,000 mt). South Korea, North Korea, Hong Kong, and Indonesia have been important markets for China's wheat exports. In marketing year 2003/04, China became a net wheat importer again, with net purchases totaling about 1 mmt.

Canada's share of China's imports in 2001/02 was 71%, compared to 16% in 2000/01. A large Canadian sale of over 400,000 mt in 2001/01 was a result of a government-to-government "special arrangement," rather than due to commercial reasons.

Wheat stocks in China are a national secret and as a result there are no published statistics on reserve stocks. The USDA estimated that ending wheat stocks were 62.4 mmt at the end of 2002/03, dropping to 43.7 mmt by the end of 2003/04.[45]

As part of China's entry into the WTO, China's government agreed to introduce a tariff rate quota (TRQ) for wheat imports. The 2002 TRQ import volume is 8.5 mmt, increasing to 9.0 mmt in 2003, and 9.6 mmt in 2004. Wheat imports within the TRQ are to be assessed a low 1% tariff. A significant aspect of China's wheat TRQ is that 10% of the quota is to be allocated to the private trade, outside of COFCO's control. However, the private quota allocation was recently announced and import rights to the 850,000 mt were allocated to over 200 firms within China. This gives each firm the ability to import a trivial amount, just over 4,000 mt. In addition, there are limits on trading the import quotas. The impact of the TRQ on wheat imports is therefore highly uncertain. The grain marketing system remains inefficient and whether or not domestic mills can use the TRQ system to substitute away from low quality domestic wheat and towards imported wheat is uncertain. For calendar year 2002 and 2003, the actual quota fill rate was extremely low (8% in 2002 and 5% in 2003).

Flour mills in China sometimes blend imported wheat with domestic wheat and the blend ratios vary considerably. The imported soft wheats are used for biscuit and cake flour and imported hard wheats are used for bread flour. The gluten level is important for domestic mills. Some flour millers are beginning to contract with domestic farmers to try and provide an incentive for growers to produce higher quality wheat. Given the inefficient grain marketing system in China, the mills are unable to dictate the classes of wheat that they purchase. The mills choices are limited and periodically some imported wheat is released from government reserves. In some cases, this imported wheat is auctioned off to local mills. The state-owned grain reserve system strives to fetch high prices for the imported wheat because most of it has been sitting in storage for a few years and has incurred high storage costs. Some of the imported wheat in 2004 also entered the state grain reserve system.

China leads the world in biotechnology research, including genetic engineering and its application to agriculture. Commercial GM crops in China include cotton, tomatoes, fresh flowers, and green peppers. GM research is ongoing with the following crops: wheat, rice, corn, soybeans, potatoes, Chinese cabbage, and tobacco. China's scientists have insect and disease resistant GM rice in field trials. These crops could be commercially grown within a few years if approved for commercial production by the Chinese government.

About 60% of China's cotton acreage was planted to GM Bt cotton in marketing year 2003. A large number of Bt cotton varieties are being grown in China. Cotton farmers are much better off due to lower costs, higher yields, and reduced exposure to harmful chemicals. In addition, there is a positive environmental impact associated with reduced chemical application to cotton.

China has over 20% of the world's rice area and at the present time China's farmers spend about $150 (USD) per hectare for chemical control of insects and diseases. Despite this significant expenditure on chemical control, China still loses up to 10% of its potential crop each year due to insects and diseases. Strip stem borer and brown plant hopper are the two main insects that destroy a portion of the rice crop every year.

China's scientists are also working on disease resistance and insect resistant (winter) wheat. The yellow dwarf virus is a serious problem for wheat in China and a GM wheat resistant to this disease is under development. Aphids transmit the yellow dwarf rice and GM wheat research is also focusing on developing aphid resistant wheat. Wheat viruses are spreading to more and more regions of China and pose a serious problem. Other important wheat diseases include powdery mildew and rust.

The GM wheat research is transferring genes from wild species into common wheat. In some cases, marker assisted breeding is then used to further develop additional lines. Marker assisted breeding is not strictly genetic engineering, but it is combined with genetic engineering techniques.

Research on GM corn in China is focusing on producing insect and disease resistant corn. In addition, research is trying to improve the quality of corn. Genetic modification of corn is aimed at raising the lysine content of corn. Higher lysine content would improve the feeding value of corn.

The approval process for GM crops in China consists of four stages. The first stage requires permission for laboratory research. The second stage involves field trials for relatively small areas. The third stage permits field trials covering larger areas and varietal approval. Finally, the fourth stage entails Ministry of Agriculture (National Biosafety Committee) approval for commercial release. Both the rice and wheat GM research is at the second stage, but the rice program is ahead of the wheat program. Transgenic research on rice is less complicated compared to that on wheat because it is easier to transfer genes in rice compared to wheat.

A certain amount of Chinese tofu and soya sauce is made with imported GM soybeans. Imports account for close to 50% of the consumption of soybeans in China, with imports originating in the United States, Brazil, and Argentina. Some of the Chinese soya sauce production made from imported soybeans is exported to the EU.

In 2001, China issued rules requiring certification, registration and labeling of certain biotech foods and feed products. Many of the details of the biotech labeling and certification rules remain unresolved.

South Korea
Unlike the case in Japan or China, the private sector controls wheat imports into Korea and there is only a small wheat import tariff of about 2%. The wheat mills in Korea negotiate directly with foreign suppliers. In

a typical year, Korea imports about 2.4 mmt. of milling wheat from Australia, Canada, the EU. The United States enjoys the largest market share (55%), Australia accounts for about 40% and Canada is a relatively small supplier (about 5 to 6% of the import market).

The US sells white wheat, HRW, and DNS into the Korean market. Australia sells Australian soft, standard white, and hard wheat. Canada sells CWRS, primarily No. 2 (or better). The cif price for CWRS (13.5%) paid by Korean millers is normally about the same as the DNS (14%) price out of the United States.

Australia's market share of Korea's milling wheat imports has increased from 20% to 40% in the last decade. At the same time, the US market share has declined, but is still high. This development is reportedly due to aggressive price cutting strategies by the Australian Wheat Board.

There are eight flour-milling companies in Korea, with 11 plants. The combined milling capacity of the 11 plants is 10,185 mt. per day. The three largest milling companies account for 68% of Korea's total milling capacity. These three companies are Daehan F.M. Co. (29%), Cheil Jedang Corp. (24%), and Dongah F.M. Co. (15%).

In addition to the 2.4 mmt of milling wheat imports each year, Korea imports a significant amount of feed wheat in some years. Feed wheat imports totaled 809,400 mt. in 2000 and 1,141,100 in 2001. Canada accounted for about 17% of feed wheat imports in 2000 and 2001, which means that Canada sells more feed wheat than milling wheat to Korea. In recent years, Korean feed imports also have been sourced from Eastern Europe, India and China.

In Korea, wheat is milled for "all purpose" flour (66.5%), bread flour (17%), and cake flour (16.5%). All-purpose flour is used for the popular instant noodles. The bread flour is used primarily for frozen dough products purchased by bakeries. Typically, CWRS is blended with DNS for the production of bread flour. There is a wide range of blending ratios, with CWRS accounting for anywhere from 20% to 100% of the bread flour. The actual blend depends on what the end user wants. McDonalds restaurants reportedly require 100% CWRS for their hamburger buns.

Cake flour in Korea is produced mainly from US western white (WW), with some additional US soft white (SW) and Australian soft (AS) wheat.

The mills produce all-purpose flour from the following wheat classes: US hard red winter (HRW), WW, SW, AS and Australian Hard (AH).

Wheat flour products in Korea compete in the marketplace with rice and rice is highly protected. The farm gate price of rice in Korea was over $1600/mt in 2002, compared to the world price of about $300/mt.

Korea has two sets of mandatory GM labeling regulations. One set applies to unprocessed food and is administered by the Ministry of Agriculture and Forestry. These regulations apply to the following unprocessed commodities: corn, soybeans, bean sprouts, and potatoes. These were introduced in 2001 and extended to potatoes in 2002.

In addition, the Korea Food and Drug Administration (KFDA) has mandatory labeling that applies to a list of 27 processed food products containing corn, soybeans, bean sprouts, or potatoes as one of the top five ingredients in the particular food product. The tolerance level is 3%, which means that processed foods may contain less than 3% GM material and be exempted from labeling. In addition, products such as soybean oil, corn oil, soya sauce, and corn syrup are exempted from GM labeling requirements. However, recent DNA tests in Korea found GM material in corn syrup and there is ongoing discussion of whether or not corn syrup should be labeled. The Korea Food and Drug Administration (KFDA) regulations stipulate that processed food products should be labeled if recombinant DNAs or foreign proteins are present in the final products.[46] Voluntary labeling of non-GM food products is not allowed.

The Korean government is promoting biotechnology and its use in agriculture. Research is being conducted on the following GM foods: rice, wheat, cabbage, Chinese cabbage, tomatoes, lettuce, red peppers, sesame, garlic, watermelons, and apples. This suggests that the Korean government believes that GM technology has great potential for food products and government statements reinforce that implication.

Approximately 400,000 mt. of non-GM soybeans are imported in Korea each year for human consumption, primarily in the form of tofu. Korean soybean food processors demand non-GM soybeans. These imports are controlled by a state-trading agency, the Agricultural and Fisheries Marketing Corporation (AFMC), under a (favorable) tariff rate quota. The state trader tenders every three months for non-GM soybeans and 6 or 7 private companies bid for this business.

Almost all of the non-GM food soybeans are imported from the United States, but South America and China are also suppliers. The US industry is able to provide segregated soybeans and has implemented a certification system to guarantee the soybeans are non-GM. An export certificate is provided with each cargo, indicating the soybeans are non-GM. Approximately 25% of US soybean exports to Korea are non-GM varieties. The AFMC reportedly pays a price premium of approximately 10% for the non-GM soybeans.[47]

Korea also imports about 9 mmt of corn each year, of which about 2 mmt (over 20%) is for non-feed processing and food use. Most of the 2 mmt imports are non-GM, sourced from the US, China or Brazil. The US segregation system that meets Japan's non-GM needs for corn also works for the S. Korean market.

Korea is a rapidly developing country with an aging farm population. In all likelihood, the acreage devoted to agriculture will decline significantly. Korea has a substantial net trade deficit in agricultural and food products and a large and growing net trade deficit in grains and oilseeds. Korea is potentially very important to Canadian agriculture as an export market. Korea is willing to accept biotechnological developments in food production.

Economics of Wheat Substitutability
The major classes of wheat traded internationally include hard red spring (HRS), hard red winter (HRW), soft red winter (SRW), and white (both soft and hard). When considering the effects of the introduction of GM spring wheat in Canada or in North America, an important issue is the degree to which different wheats are substitutes (e.g., CWRS versus US DNS, or CWRS versus HRW). If two types of wheat are highly substitutable, then a buyer can easily switch from one source to another when sourcing its wheat grist. So an importer of CWRS could choose to buy from other sources if GM spring wheat is introduced in Canada and if the resulting premium for non-GM CWRS is too high. For instance, the CWB contends that wheat from other exporting countries is not a close substitute for CWRS, and this is the main reason that the CWB claims that it can price discriminate across markets. If the price discrimination argument is correct, then wheat from other exporting countries is not easily substituted for Canadian wheat, and buyers may have little choice but to continue buying Canadian wheat after the introduction of GM wheat.

Economists usually measure the degree of substitutability in two ways: the elasticity of substitution and the cross-price elasticity. To calculate these elasticities, the first step is the estimation of a demand or production function, then the elasticities are derived from the estimated parameters. Neither of these approaches measures the market response to a one-time event like the introduction of GM wheat. Instead, both of these approaches measure how the market responds to price changes.

The cross-price elasticity is a measure of how much the quantity demand for a good changes when the price of another good changes. For example, if the price of wheat from the US increases, buyers might choose to buy more Canadian wheat. That would mean that US and Canadian wheat are substitutes, and the cross-price elasticity would be positive. Elasticities measure responsiveness to price changes using percentages, rather than physical quantities. The cross-price elasticity measures the percentage increase in sales of a good when the price of a substitute increases by one percent. If the cross-price elasticity of Canadian wheat with respect to the price of US wheat were 10 in a particular market, then we would expect that a one percent increase in the price of US wheat, holding the Canadian price constant, would cause Canadian sales to increase by 10% to that market.

The demand elasticity facing the CWB in any given market is typically more elastic, the smaller is Canada's share in that market. For example, consider the US market, an important source of foreign demand for Canadian wheat. If the US domestic demand elasticity for milling wheat from all sources is –0.2 and the supply elasticity in the United States is 1.0, then, with a 4 percent market share, the import demand elasticity facing Canada would be about –31.[48] Canada's average market share in the world wheat trade is about 15 percent, so if the absolute value of both the demand and supply elasticity in importing nations (aggregated together) is 1.0, then the elasticity facing Canada is about –12. Thus, in general, we believe that import demand elasticities for Canadian wheat are large in absolute value. When the elasticity of demand is large, gains from any attempts at price discrimination are correspondingly small because reductions in sales volume in any given market have very small impacts on prices in that market. Said differently, a small percentage increase in the price of CWRS in such a market would cause a large percentage reduction in quantity demanded.

In fact, if import demand elasticities for wheat from individual exporting countries are large, this means that world wheat markets are competitive and there is almost no scope for export STEs like the CWB to exercise monopoly power. We maintain that there is supporting evidence for this position. A US Department of Agriculture (1986) study of the 1980 embargo on shipments of grain to the Former Soviet Union (FSU) concluded that the embargo had almost no effect on world wheat markets. The reason was that wheat from one export source was readily substitutable for wheat from another export source; that is, wheat from different exporting countries was highly substitutable and, therefore, elasticities of import demand for wheat from any given exporting country were large.

It is very difficult to measure wheat import demand elasticities with precision due to the fact that the necessary data on prices and volumes are not publicly available, particularly in Canada. Carter, MacLaren, and Yilmaz (1999) used the best available public data and tested for any evidence of imperfect competition in the Japanese wheat import market. They allowed for various possible forms of imperfect competition and presented a set of alternative theoretical models of the Japanese market for wheat imports in which account was taken of various forms of strategic interaction among Australian, Canadian and United States exporters. They tested for the type of strategic interaction that is most consistent with the data. Overall, their findings suggested that the competitive model as a characterization of the wheat market cannot be ruled out.

The elasticity of substitution is more complicated. The elasticity of substitution directly measures the degree to which two goods are substituted for each other, but the interpretation is more difficult. The elasticity of substitution is the ratio of two ratios. For import demand, the elasticity of substitution measures the percent change in the ratio of imports of good 1 and 2 for a one percent change in the ratio of price of goods 1 and 2. For example, the elasticity of substitution between Canadian and US wheat would measure the percentage change in the Canadian/US import ratio caused by a one percent change in the ratio of Canadian/US prices. An elasticity of substitution of 10, for example, would mean that a one percent change in the Canadian/US relative price of wheat would cause a ten percent change in the ratio of wheat sold.

The importance of the elasticity of substitution is most easily seen by considering two extremes. With two goods, the lowest possible elasticity of substitution is zero. In this case, the two goods are not substitutes at all. Even if the relative prices changed, meaning that one gets cheaper with respect to the other, the imports of the two goods do not change. If they were purchased in a three to one ratio before the price change, they are purchased in a three to one ratio after the price change. The quantities imported may change, but they will always be used in the same ratio. If the elasticity of substitution were infinite, then the two goods would be perfect substitutes. That means that the slightest change in price would cause the importer to purchase only the cheaper of the two goods. They would be considered essentially the same good, and whichever one is cheaper is the one that will be chosen. It is rare to find an estimated elasticity of substitution at either of these two extremes. The more common comparison is whether the substitution between the two goods is "elastic" (elasticity of substitution greater than one) or "inelastic" (elasticity of substitution between zero and one). Inelastic means that the change in the use ratio is less than the change in relative prices, indicating that it is difficult to substitute between the two goods. The closer to zero is the elasticity of substitution; the harder it is for a user to substitute one good for another.

This may be clarified with a more detailed numerical example. Assume the elasticity of substitution is 10, as above, and that Canada sells 20,000 mt of wheat to a country, while the US sells 10,000 mt to the same country, so the ratio of wheat sold is 2. Now, assume that the Canadian wheat sells for $200 per ton, and the US wheat for $100 per ton, so the price ratio is also 2. The elasticity of substitution of 10 tells us that one percent change in the relative price will cause a ten percent change in the sales ratio. So if the price of Canadian wheat were to decrease by one percent to $198, the highest possible new level of sales for Canadian wheat would be 22,000 mt (a 10% increase), but it is more likely that sales of US wheat would also drop, indicating the increase in Canadian sales would be lower. After the price change, however, the ratio of Canadian to US imports will be 2.2, 10% higher than the old ratio.

Both of these elasticity measures deal strictly with the responsiveness of consumption patterns to price changes, but they actually reveal much more than that. If the quantity demanded is not sensitive to price changes, it is unlikely to be sensitive to other changes, such as the different prices resulting from the introduction of GM wheat.

Unfortunately, calculating elasticities of substitution for wheat is very difficult, and so little economic research has been conducted on the subject. There are two primary difficulties. First, it is reasonable to think that the market for imported wheat is different for every importing country, so the estimation might have to be done for each country individually. Countries can be aggregated into regions, but that causes another set of difficulties, discussed below. In addition, elasticities would need to be calculated pairwise for every country of interest, and possibly for the different classes of wheat as well. Limiting the analysis to a smaller subset of the total market, like hard spring wheat, has its own difficulties. Estimation requires reliable data on the amount sold and the selling prices. Price and quantity data (by class) from Canada, one of the major exporters of hard spring wheat, is not available in sufficient detail to be useful.

Relevant economic Studies on substitutability
A recent paper on wheat demand which provides useful information is by Koo, Mao and Sakurai (2001). They use a translog cost function to estimate demand by the Japanese milling industry for wheat, differentiated by class and country of origin. They emphasize that they are using an approach grounded in production theory to generate their estimation equations. The justification is that wheat is not a consumer-ready food product; instead it is an input to production for millers that produce wheat flour. This is in contrast to most other studies that use an approach based on consumer theory.

Koo, Mao and Sakurai do not consider feed wheat or durum wheat, and estimate 7 input and 3 output translog cost function for the Japanese flour milling industry. The seven inputs are wheat varieties (domestic soft wheat, US soft wheat, US semi-hard wheat, US hard wheat, Canadian hard wheat and Australian soft wheat) and labor. They ignore other inputs, such as energy and capital. The three outputs are three different types of flour: weak, strong and standard.

Table 2.4 shows the elasticities of substitution estimated by Koo et.al. Because the elasticities of substitution are symmetric, only the lower half of the table is filled out. An asterisk indicates that the estimated elasticity is significantly different from zero at the 0.05 percent significance level. The elasticity of substitution between U.S and Canadian Hard wheats is positive and significant (26.14), meaning that they are highly competitive with one another. As a reminder, the elasticity of substitution of 26.14 says that if Canadian wheat became more expensive relative to US wheat by one percent, the ratio of Canadian to US wheat sales would fall by 26.14 percent. Soft wheats also have positive elasticities of substitution, so the results indicate that they compete with each other as well. The hard and soft wheats have a negative elasticity of substitution, but the estimates are not significant, except for Australian soft wheat and US hard and semi-hard. Unlike the two good case described earlier, when there are more than two goods, elasticities of substitution can be negative.

Table 2.4. Wheat Elasticity of Substitution Estimates for Japan

	Domestic Soft	US Soft	US Semi-hard	US Hard	Canadian Hard	Australian Soft	Labor
Domestic Soft	-66.64*						
US Soft	25.89*	-16.23*					
US Semi-hard	19.96*	10.11*	-66.63*				
US Hard	-6.35	-3.96*	16.21	-33.44*			
Canadian Hard	-3.01	-5.03	18.09	26.14*	-40.49*		
Australian Soft	7.42	5.64*	-15.58*	11.60*	4.38	-25.33*	
Labor	-2.53*	1.81*	2.11	-0.66	1.39	4.03*	-7.60*

Source: Koo, Mao, and Sakurai

Table 2.5 gives own- and cross-price elasticities estimated by Koo et. al. The estimates of cross-price elasticities provide a similar picture. The cross-price elasticities are positive between US hard and Canadian hard wheat (meaning they are substitutes) and large (an elasticity greater than one means that change in the price of one source causes a greater than proportional change in demand for wheat from the other source). The result of Koo, Mao and Sakurai is that wheats of different degrees of hardness are complements, and wheats of the same (or similar) hardness are substitutes.

Table 2.5. Wheat Price Elasticities for Japan

	Factor Price						
	Domestic Soft	US Soft	US Semi-hard	US Hard	Canadian Hard	Australian Soft	Labor
Demand:							
Domestic Soft	-6.59*	5.18*	2.36*	-1.11	-0.46	0.94	-0.32*
US Soft	2.56*	-3.25*	1.19*	-0.96	-0.76*	.072*	0.23*
US Semi-hard	1.97*	2.02*	-7.86*	2.84	2.75	-1.99*	0.27
US Hard	-0.63*	-0.79	1.91	- 5.86*	3.97*	1.48*	-0.08
Canadian Hard	-0.297	-1.01*	2.13	4.58*	-6.15	0.56	0.18
Australian Soft	0.73	1.13*	-1.84*	2.03*	0.67	-3.24*	0.52*
Labor	-0.25*	0.36*	0.25	-0.12	0.21	0.52*	-0.98

Source: Koo, Mao and Sakurai

Table 2.6. Wilson's Estimates of Wheat Price Elasticities

Type	CWRS	HRS	WHI	ASW	HRW
			Indonesia		
CWRS	2.8	-3.34	1.56	.58	-1.64
HRS	-1.85	-5.4	2.49	2.51	2.27
White	1.62	4.68	-3.11	-7.03	3.84
ASW	.18	1.41	-2.08	.83	-.32
HRW	-1.22	30.6	-2.75	-.77	-3.8
			Japan		.
CWRS	.05	-.02	-.25	.13	.09
HRS	-.02	-.53	.99	-.21	.27
White	-.34	.76	-1.21	.83	-.25
ASW	.19	-.76	.92	-.61	.25
HRW	.09	.21	.21	.18	-.28
			Korea		
CWRS	.93	.86	-1.55	-4.26	-4.02
HRS	1.06	1.35	5.30	2.12	-.98
White	-.41	1.15	-2.42	1.60	.08
ASW	-7.5	3.02	10.47	-4.23	1.76
HRW	1.72	-3.41	.13	-.43	1.99
			Malaysia		
CWRS	6.33	-3.10	-1.47	-1.76	
HRS	-1.96	-2.75	3.85	.86	
White	-2.98	12.38	-10.26	.86	
ASW	-.09	.07	.62	-.001	
			Philippines		
CWRS	-63.3	39.02	62.93	-38.63	
HRS	-.23	.63	-.41	.01	
White	-2.18	-2.39	4.56	.01	
ASW	15.81	.84	.14	-.16	
			Taiwan		
CWRS	.78	3.49	-.65		-3.62
HRS	.98	-1.66	.50		.18
White	-.29	.81	-1.34		.83
ASW					
HRW	-.80	.14	.40		.25

Source: Wilson (1994)

Wilson (1994) used a translog expenditure function to derive demand functions for different classes of wheat from different countries of the Pacific Rim, using data from 1976/77 through 1988/89. The countries included in his analysis are Hong Kong, Indonesia, Japan, Korea, Malaysia, Philippines, Singapore, Taiwan and Thailand. The wheat classes included are hard red winter, hard red spring and white from the US, CWRS from Canada and Australian standard white. Using the flexible functional form is a strength of this study, but the data have some weaknesses. The author uses FOB data from the point of export, and adds an estimate of transportation costs. Wilson is aware that Canadian and Australian price data are not transactions data, so he estimated "realized" prices for these sources.Wilson estimated price elasticities for those countries where the impact of price on the expenditure shares was significant (see Table 2.6).

In some countries, the own-price elasticities are close to zero (Japan, Hong Kong, Singapore and Thailand). Considering cross-price elasticities, there is more substitution among the white wheats than the others. CWRS is a strong substitute with HRS and WHI in the Philippines, and a strong complement to ASW in Korea and the Philippines, and HRW in Taiwan.

Hjort (1988) investigated the import substitution between classes of wheat and between sources (countries) of wheat. Hjort's primary concern was that previous studies used regional aggregation to simplify the analysis, and many assumed that wheat is a homogeneous product. Hjort points out that countries that seem quite similar have a very different pattern in wheat imports, often not importing the same classes of wheat, and rarely from the same exporters. Hjort's point is well taken, but by choosing to disaggregate so much, she is unable to estimate elasticities of substitution for many countries, due to lack of data and other econometric problems. These problems made it impossible for her to estimate substitution elasticities for some of the major hard wheat importers, such as Venezuela, the USSR and the Philippines, which accounted for 22% of imports during the time period covered by her study. Even so, there are some interesting results in her work. For example, the average elasticity of substitution between US and Canadian hard wheats (weighted by quantity imported) is 22.78, which is much higher than elasticities of substitution for other wheat classes. Referring to previous work by Patterson, she compares this to a substitution elasticity of 10 as the level that approximates a perfectly competitive market. For hard wheats, and using the cutoff elasticity of 10, import demands can be adequately represented by considering hard wheat to be homogeneous in all import markets.

Hedonic Approaches

Studies like the ones mentioned above require data on imports and prices to be estimated econometrically. An alternative approach is to use hedonic analysis. There are several economic studies that use hedonic analysis to find values for characteristics that are not priced explicitly. These papers find a value for wheat attributes, rather than an elasticity of substitution. One of the characteristics used in these models is country of origin. A price premium for wheat from Canada tells us something, but not the reasons for the price premium. In a hedonic model, it is impossible to tell whether the premium is from some important characteristic of Canadian wheat (something that would be hard to substitute away from) or a result of marketing activities, such as over-supplying protein or providing very clean wheat. Unless the values of these attributes are also estimated, then it is impossible to separate out the effects.

Wilson (1989) estimated a hedonic model of wheat differentiation in world wheat markets. The quality measures considered were habit (spring vs. winter), type (hard vs. soft), protein content and country of origin, and the time period was 1972/73 – 1986/87. He found that Canadian wheat commanded a premium in some markets (up to about $20 per metric ton in the EU), but the regressions leave out important quality factors (like dockage, foreign material and non-millable material). He found that these other factors may drive the results for the Canadian premium, since Canadian wheat has only 25-50% of the dockage and foreign material levels than is typical for US wheat.[49]

Wilson and Gallagher (1990) also measured price response and substitutability in the world wheat market. They used a demand system by Case to generate equations explaining the market share of each type of wheat in a country. These equations have market share on the left-hand side; the right-hand side is a function of the prices of all the wheat types. This model allows the estimation of the elasticities of substitution and measures of relative preferences between different types.

The wheat varieties considered in the Wilson and Gallagher study were from Australia, Argentina, the EU, CWRS, and five classes from the US. There were four markets studied: Japan, the US, Latin American and Asia (excluding Japan). The data were from the 24-year period of 1961-62 through 1984/85.

The results show that Asia was the most price responsive market, meaning there was a higher degree of substitutability there than in the other markets. The market that was the least price responsive was Japan. The primary result of this analysis is to answer the question: does a particular variety have the ability to command a price premium? In Asia, CWRS was found to command a moderate price premium relative to the other classes (these were all pairwise comparisons). In Latin America, CWRS was dominated by US HRW, but enjoyed a considerable price premium relative to wheat from the EU and US soft red winter. They found there was a very strong preference for CWRS over US white. In Japan, CWRS was found to have the ability to command a moderate price premium over other classes. The authors take pains to point out that these are not preferences for "high quality" per se, but for specific quality attributes.

Wilson and Preszler (1993) developed a linear programming model of a UK miller's decision among US HRS 14% and HRS 15%, Canadian CWRS 13.5% and 14.5%, and domestic (UK) wheat. This is not a hedonic paper in the normal sense. Instead, Wilson and Preszler use the hedonic equations as a starting point for deriving their linear programming model of the UK miller's decision. The quality characteristics used in this model are minimum and maximum protein content, maximum ash content, and minimum farinograph absorption peak time and mix time, and minimum loaf volume and falling number. There was also a minimum of 25% UK domestic wheat required in the blend. The results of the model indicate the optimal blend is 54% CWRS 14.5%, 12.2% HRS 15%, and 34% UK domestic wheat. These results are based on the price and quality characteristics used at the time of their research; they are not necessarily the same today. CWRS 14.5% would drop out of the model if the price increased by about $9/MT (CWRS 13.5% would be used instead, and the amount of HRS 15% would increase to keep the protein content up).

Implications for Commercialization of GM Wheat In Canada
The CWB's position is that the introduction of Roundup Ready wheat would have a "devastating impact on western Canadian farmer."[50] The CWB maintains that "82 percent of Canadian farmers' markets for Canadian Western Red Spring wheat indicate they would not or could not buy GM wheat."[51] This position on the market acceptance of GM wheat is inconsistent with long-running CWB claims that most of its sales are into premium markets that could not easily substitute away from CWRS.

Table 2.7 reports the CWB list of which markets the agency says will be "lost" if GM wheat is commercialized in western Canada. The single most important market for western growers is the domestic market as 10 percent of the annual crop is sold to domestic millers and 15 percent is sold domestically as feed, on average. If GM wheat is commercialized, the share of domestic flour sales used for national "branded" products may initially prefer non-GM wheat in order to avoid any possible consumer backlash. However, it is no secret that the domestic food processing industry uses GM canola oil in most of its food products. The 15 percent of the wheat crop sold into the domestic feed market would not encounter any market resistance.

The situation in the US domestic market is much the same as in Canada. The food manufacturers in both countries are using considerable GM ingredients today, so what is different about wheat? It appears that some food manufacturers are worried about the environmental groups protesting over GM wheat and possible consumer resistance that could lead to lost sales of national brand foods. So some domestic food manufacturers say they do not want GM wheat. For them, the cost of the raw wheat (or flour) is such a small cost share item in manufacturing of most national brand foods that the processors do not see GM wheat as significantly boosting their profits. So they are acting rationally when they say they do not want to use GM wheat if there is some risk of losing a small percentage of their customer base on the national brands.

Table 2.7 CWB List of Market Acceptance/Non-Acceptance of GM Wheat in Major Canadian Wheat Markets

Country	Status	Note
Canada	Reject	Customers currently requesting non-GM certification.
Iran	Not reject	No comment received.
Japan	Reject	Customers currently requesting non-GM certification.
United States	Reject	Customers currently requesting non-GM certification.
Mexico	Reject	Customers currently requesting non-GM certification.
Indonesia	Reject	Customers currently requesting non-GM certification.
Philippines	Reject	Customers currently requesting non-GM certification.
Colombia	Reject	Customers currently requesting non-GM certification.
Venezuela	Not reject	No comment received.
United Kingdom	Reject	EU moratorium against the approval of new GM crops, customers currently requesting non-GM certification.
Guatemala	No information	
China	Reject	Pre-approval required for import.

Source: Canadian Wheat Board, September 26, 2002.

Initially, the market for domestic generic wheat products (e.g., frozen dough) and offshore developing countries offers the most potential for immediate market acceptance. This large segment of the market is more interested in the price of wheat than whether or not it is GM. If the price of non-GM wheat moves to a premium over GM wheat due to higher unit costs of production and segregation costs, then most of the domestic processors may well choose to buy GM wheat. Eventually the high-end "national brand" portion of the market may decide to buy GM wheat once there is little risk of a consumer boycott. In the meantime, Japan and the UK may pay a premium for non-GM wheat and those farmers who want to specialize in the non-GM can do so and obtain a price premium to offset the costs of segregation, higher unit costs of production, etc. This would be much like the non-GM corn and soybean markets today.

Japan, the U.K., and South Korea currently import both GM and non-GM corn and soybeans. The non-GM product is segregated and trades at a price premium to GM. In all likelihood, with the commercialization of GM wheat, Japan, the U.K. and S. Korea would import some GM and some non-GM wheat. There would be a dual marketing track and the market would soon sort out the price premium for non-GM wheat. This premium would depend on the overall demand and supply of non-GM relative to GM wheat.

In Table 2.7, the CWB lists several developing countries such as Indonesia and Mexico as "rejecting" GM wheat because they are "currently requesting non-GM certification." It is costless for these importers to make such a request and this type of request is temporary and perfunctory because these importers are being told that GM wheat is not being commercially grown anywhere.

Given the agronomic and environmental benefits of GM wheat, it will soon be commercialized somewhere in the world. If not in Canada or the United States, it will be commercialized in China, Australia, or perhaps India. For example, if saline resistant wheat is commercialized in Australia this will convert thousands of acres of marginal land into production. Western Canadian farmers are moving away from wheat due to the low profitability and the regulated nature of the market. The CWB should be doing everything possible to improve grower returns. They should look at the benefits of GM canola, for example. It has been widely accepted, grower returns have improved, and canola acreage has increased. With GM wheat, the potential yield gain and disease resistance is significant, as is potential grower return improvement. It is in both the growers' and most customers' interest to commercialize GM wheat. For the CWB staff, the status quo is in their interest. Unfortunately this is not the case for growers and most CWB customers.

Conclusion

This chapter has discussed developments in the world wheat market and we conclude that events in the past few years underscore the reality that the world grain markets are highly competitive and no single importer is dependent on Canadian wheat. This is illustrated by the fact that CWB exports to Brazil and Iran have seriously eroded in recent years, and these two countries were recently major markets for Canadian wheat. Continued wheat production increases in the former Soviet Union (FSU) will keep competitive pressure on the Canadian producers. Importers have clearly demonstrated that they can and will substitute away from Canadian wheat.

In addition, future wheat import demand growth will originate mainly from developing countries due to population growth and urbanization. Virtually all of the world's population growth in the next 30 years is expected to take place in urban areas in developing countries, and so developing country wheat imports may grow appreciably (FAO). With few exceptions, these developing countries would be indifferent between importing GM versus non-GM wheat. Instead; they care most about the price. The CWB maintains that about 82 percent of Canadian farmers' markets for Canadian Western Red Spring wheat indicate they would not or could not buy GM wheat. This CWB view ignores the fact that Canadian wheat competes mainly in lower quality markets (e.g., the Philippines and Indonesia) that are price sensitive, and where substitution among wheat grades and classes is high. We estimate that approximately 80% of the market for Canadian spring wheat would accept GM wheat, after an initial transition period. Our reasoning is based on the large share of CWB wheat exports sold into developing countries and the fact that 15 percent of the prairie wheat crop is typically sold into the domestic feed market. Most developing countries and the domestic feeders will not resist GM wheat.

This chapter has reviewed the wheat market in certain key countries, including the United Kingdom, Japan, Indonesia, China, and South Korea. We found that the United Kingdom and Japan are likely the only two import markets that would be willing to pay a price premium for non-GM wheat. Furthermore, China is likely to soon approve commercial production of GM rice and then wheat. Brazil and Argentina may also be early adopters. The adoption of genetically modified wheat and other food grains (such as GM rice) in other countries will contribute to the competitive pressure facing prairie agriculture. This competition will have a significant impact on Canadian wheat farmers because the Canadian wheat industry is driven by exports. Normally export sales account for about 70 percent of western Canada's annual wheat production.

3. SEGREGATION AND IDENTITY PRESERVATION ISSUES

The commercialization of GM wheat on the Canadian prairies is conditional upon implementation of an effective segregation or identity preservation (IP) system (Grain Industry Working Group on GM Wheat). Considerable discussion has been generated in recent years on segregation and IP in the prairie grain industry, particularly as it relates to the longstanding kernel visual distinguishability (KVD) process of segregating wheat into classes, and to the prospect of commercial GM wheat production. Some argue that segregating GM wheat on the prairies is not possible, is too expensive and cannot be administered without damage to the Canadian reputation for consistent quality in wheat (Furtan, Gray and Holzman 2003a,b). Adrian Measner, President and CEO of the CWB recently stated:

> *At present, we don't have an effective system to segregate GM wheat, nor have agreements been reached with our customers regarding acceptable tolerance levels.*
> Speech presented to the National Grain Trade Council, Quebec, September 18, 2003.

In the context of the Canadian system, Furtan, Gray and Holzman (2003a) indicated:

> *…the cost to segregate GM and non-GM wheat would be prohibitive given the current grain-handling system* (p. 440).

Earlier, Gray observed:

> *Given the relatively small per-tonne benefits from growing HT wheat relative to segregation costs, it seems unlikely that segregation could be maintained except for possibly niche markets that do not have access to foreign non-GM supplies.* (p.191)

In developing these arguments as to why segregation would be too costly for Canadian GM wheat, Furtan, Gray and Holzman (2003b), and Gray quoted Smyth and Phillips (2001) who found that segregating canola in a closed loop system would cost up to $40/mt (USD). Furtan, Gray and Holzman (2003a) rely on Downie and Beckie to argue that segregation is impossible in the case of wheat, but Downie and Beckie's estimates are for canola pedigreed seed. So the assumptions of Furtan, Gray and Holzman

(2003a,b), and Gray that segregating wheat is impossible should be strongly questioned.

Despite these bold claims by the University of Saskatchewan economists, segregation and identity preservation in the prairie grain industry is neither unique to genetically modified crops, nor a novel marketing tool in Canadian grains and oilseeds. It is successfully applied to a wide range of crops. Where it is applied, there is usually some risk to the integrity of Canadian quality standards but that risk has been successfully managed.

This section analyzes several aspects of segregation of wheat in the context of the prairie grain production, handling, and marketing system. The purpose of this analysis is to provide an assessment of the feasibility, options and costs of identity preservation when there is commercial production of GM wheat. The first part of the discussion deals with the relationship among segregation, IP and marketability of prairie grains. In this regard, the real issue is "certification" of individual lots of product, a factor which is often lost in the rhetoric of conflicting positions. The next section briefly reviews examples and experiences with segregation and IP already in place on the prairies, which illustrate that this practice is common within the Canadian bulk handling system. There have been far more economic analyses of segregation systems conducted in the United States than in Canada. We review some of the quantitative evidence that is available from the United States and the prairie region in Canada. Finally, cost estimates are provided for segregating GM wheat in sequential bulk handling with non-GM wheat for production levels of GM wheat exceeding fifty percent of total wheat output on the prairies.

Segregation, Identity Preservation And Certification Of Prairie Wheat
As explained by Smyth and Phillips (2003), the terms *identity preservation* (IP), and *segregation* are defined differently in the literature and sometimes are used interchangeably. For instance, Lin defines both identity preservation and segregation differently than do Smyth and Phillips (2003). Compared to Smyth and Phillips, Lin has a narrower definition of IP and a broader definition of segregation. Lin defines an IP system as a closed handling process that begins with a producer contract and requires strict separation (such as the use of containers for transport) at all times. Alternatively, Lin defines segregation as the requirement "that crops be kept separate to avoid commingling during planting, harvesting, loading and unloading, storage and transport."

In contrast to Lin, Smyth and Phillips (2003) maintain that segregation systems are not designed to capture price premiums. Rather, they define segregation systems as typically being part of regulatory standards and "can be developed as part of a variety registration process, where government regulators use contract registration to ensure that certain novel varieties will not enter the handling system of like varieties."

According to *Milling and Baking News* (2001):[52]

> *Segregation refers to a system in which grains, both genetically altered and non-genetically altered, are kept separate to avoid commingling during harvesting, loading and unloading, storing and transporting.*

This same source describes IP as:

> *... a trace-back procedure that begins with an agreement between a farmer and a contracting agent ... designated cars and trucks are analyzed at all transfer points to ensure the identity-preserved product has not come in contact with non-identity preserved product. IP typically requires containerized shipping be maintained at all times.*

We do not attempt to settle this definitional debate here but rather note that typically an identity preservation (IP) system is more comprehensive than a segregation system. In the extreme, an IP system identifies the source and variety of the grain and maintains that identity throughout the handling and processing system. A less stringent IP system is one where a crop is grown, usually under contract, and handled under controlled conditions so that the end user of the product is assured that it has maintained its unique identity. Alternatively, a segregation system keeps a given variety or type of grain apart from others. An IP system is typically more expensive than a segregation system. However, sometimes a segregation system is loosely defined as an IP system. In any case, common usage of the two definitions is overlapping and so the two terms are often used interchangeably.

We maintain that segregation, identity preservation and certification of Canadian wheat are a continuum of marketing activities performed to create value in relation to where the wheat is sold and for what purpose. There are three aspects of value creation that are important in wheat: the inherent qualitative characteristics (including uniformity within and between lots) of the wheat; the absence of all forms of foreign material which have undesirable characteristics in terms of end use; and the ability to provide buyer assurance of qualitative characteristics (and increasingly, food safety) in relation to individual cargoes of wheat. "Segregation" is a term that is usually understood with regard to prairie grains to mean grade standards and the grading process. The GM debate refers to the separation of GM from non-GM grain, where price premiums for non-GM may develop. "Grain cleaning and purity requirements" protect against foreign material. "Certification" assures integrity of individual cargoes.

An existing "segregation process" is overseen by the Canadian Grain Commission (CGC) which administers grouping and preservation of wheat varieties into grades in commercial channels. The CGC also *certifies* quality of wheat cargoes at point of transfer to end-use buyers, dealers or importers. This process is based on the kernel visual distinguishability (KVD) model–if a particular sample of wheat looks like a particular class, it must be of that class or it will not be legally marketed. KVD has generally been considered to be an effective tool for segregation but it is also a blunt marketing instrument with undesirable side-effects.[53] As of 2004, wheat is the only prairie grain which remains primarily dependent on KVD. Other grains and oilseeds, when segregation is required, have moved beyond KVD to "specification buying" and various forms and levels of identity preservation. Even wheat segregation is not completely dependent on KVD as the large seed market, several CWB contracts, and the Warburton contract, all use various forms of segregation and IP. The CGC proposed a replacement for KVD in 2003, Varietal Eligibility Declaration (VED), which would have been a compulsory declaration and monitoring form of IP, but the proposal was later withdrawn.

The second aspect of segregation, *unintended foreign matter*,[54] is normally thought of in the context of weed seeds, other grains (including different wheat varieties), inseparable seeds, dirt, stones and the like which result in cleaning (and cleaning standards) for grade categories established and administered by the CGC. This aspect of segregation has direct significance for GM wheat because it is the risk of presence of inseparable GM wheat in non-GM lots that generates arguments against introduction of GM wheat. Unintended foreign matter finds its way into cargoes (adventitious presence is the term used for genetically modified foreign matter) by mechanical means (accidentally or incidentally) or by genetic means.[55] As the risk of out-crossing is low and control costs of herbicide tolerant weeds are manageable (Remple and McNulty), the critical link in segregation, as long as there is public or market resistance to GM wheat, is identity preservation of conventional wheat and/or GM wheat.

Identity preservation is an extension of segregation of product as described above, refining the objective and segregating in much more detail, often for a very specific purpose. While segregation in wheat in Canada is usually regulated by the CGC, identity preservation is generally a tool of commercial trade and marketing, practiced for the most part outside the CGC by grain buyers, millers, malsters, processors and the Canadian Wheat Board (CWB). IP comes in many forms and degrees of detail and has become a common marketing tool in the grain trade. The scope and nature of Canadian IP and segregation programs are discussed in a later section.

The purpose of segregating wheat or any grain is to capture the best end use and so add or maximize value. This principle is played out in a commercial world with imperfect information, random events, and human or equipment error. Consequently, the standards that exist on segregation and identity preservation usually have *tolerances* for unintended material, dockage, damaged and diseased kernels, other grains and the like. Buyers usually will specify tolerances, and as the regulator of wheat quality standards, the CGC establishes and maintains tolerances on wheat. There are few examples of zero tolerance on foreign matter in the grain system, although the "top" export grade on Canadian wheat requires zero dockage. That is a misleading requirement however, since there is an allowance for "foreign matter" because it is recognized that absolute purity is usually impossible in commercial systems. Reasonable tolerances are a critical variable in the feasibility of any commercially viable IP system.[56] There are no tolerances that have been established on GM material in wheat because GM wheat is not yet commercialized anywhere. However, many importing countries do have tolerances for approved GM crops and for labeling of non-GM products. For example, Mexico recently signed an agreement with the United States and Canada that covers imports of GM corn. Mexico has established a tolerance level of 5 percent on raw product corn shipments and if the 5 percent is exceeded the cargo must carry a label that says it "may contain" GM material.

The final and most important component of this general discussion of IP is *certification*: certification that the product is as claimed, that it meets whatever specifications are imposed by the official standards or by the transaction, that it is safe for the use intended, and that there are no unknown components. Certification has legal and liability implications for the parties to the transaction, and effective certification reduces transactions costs in grain trading. In the context of GM and non-GM wheat, the certification issue is to assure that buyers who distinguish between the two types of wheat have confidence that the product meets their specification. Certification of Canadian wheat is a responsibility of the CGC within established grades and procedures but additional certification may be provided by the seller. Under present grade standards on prairie grain, if GM wheat were registered in the CWRS class, GM or GM-free status would have to be certified by the seller as no Canadian standards currently exist in relation to genetic modification. If VED, or a similar official declaration and monitoring process were implemented on all wheat categories by the CGC, the process of wheat certification would be enhanced.

The introduction of GM wheat at any level on the prairies would result in at least two sets of buyers: those who would buy only non-GM wheat (at specified tolerance levels), and those who would willingly buy GM wheat. In all likelihood, tolerance levels (of GM wheat in non-GM cargoes) would vary according to the final destination. But there would likely be a third set of buyers–those who would switch product allegiance according to price differentials. We assume that traditional wheat, i.e., non-GM, would have a price premium at least until buyers and consumers become comfortable with the new technology. Throughout this discussion, we assume that the economics of mixing GM and non GM product is non-symmetric, i.e., there are no negative consequences of non-GM wheat in GM cargoes, but GM wheat in non-GM cargoes beyond specified tolerances has negative economic consequences. The segregation problem then is to assure that the presence of bio-tech DNA or protein of the raw or processed product falls within the tolerances specified by the buyers, and cargoes can be certified to be within these specifications.

Development of a segregation system must meet these objectives in a commercially feasible manner. Most analysts assume that it is the non-GM product that is "at risk" of mixing with GM wheat, and therefore it is the non-GM wheat that must be kept separate. That proposition may not be the most cost-effective in the early stages of technology adoption when GM wheat is the smaller crop. We suggest that effective IP on the GM wheat (which would have lower volume initially), accompanied by monitoring and testing to assure purity of the traditional (larger) volume crop, should provide assurances required for certification of the non-GM product during the first two or three years of adoption.[57]

There are several essential features of a system (or process) which would be applied to assure that wheat produced in a mixed GM and non-GM environment could be certified IP (American Seed Trade Association, undated probably 2002; Dahl and Wilson, 2002; Wilson et al. January 2003) :

- field conditions and agronomic practices that avoid and prevent adventitious presence or spread of GM wheat;
- purity of seed;
- minimum out-crossing at time of pollination and flower fertilization;[58]
- "clean machines" at all levels of seeding, harvesting, transportation, handling and storage;
- purity at and in processing to prevent mixing of different wheats and introduction of biotech derived DNA or protein from non-wheat sources;
- security on process at all critical points in the system to avoid mistakes, and monitoring to ensure conditions are met;
- cost efficient testing procedures at critical points of exchange;
- non-zero, commercial tolerance levels; and certification standards and procedures.

Each of these steps is essential to an acceptable and dependable IP system of the integrity required for separating GM and non-GM wheat. Naturally there is an overriding constraint on what and how much is done: as in any other value-creation process, it must be economically feasible. The ideal IP system is unlikely to be one that guarantees zero tolerance because that would be very expensive. The ideal system is one which "gets the job done" and leaves enough financial margin to induce appropriate economic response.

To conclude this discussion we note three new institutional (regulatory) developments on Canadian grains that would reinforce the ability to keep biotech derived DNA and protein separate from conventional wheat. First, the VED system proposed by CGC was intended to assure class purity (not varietal purity as the name implies); it would have been applied at each transfer of ownership throughout the marketing system, achieved by seller declaration (an affidavit). VED also implies traceback capability.[59] VED would have, therefore, contributed directly to any IP system on wheat.[60] Since both GM and non-GM varieties would have been subject to VED, protection against mixing of product would come from both GM and non-GM sides. The proposal for a VED system was terminated at the end of 2003 on the basis of some benefit-cost analysis conducted on the proposal.[61]

Second, the CGC has also developed IP protocol to support private IP initiatives and the international ISO protocols–the Canadian Identity Preserved Recognition System. This program was launched in 2003, is voluntary, and already has been used by some soybean dealers in Ontario and Quebec as an audit certification process. According to the background brochure:

> the CGC's certification of IP processes will provide buyers an added level of assurance that IP shipments will meet their specialized quality requirements.[62]

Totally separate from this initiative, at least one of the large prairie grain companies has implemented ISO compatible procedures in its grain purchases. Individual truck unload samples are retained until the product has moved to the next stage of marketing which means that producer deliveries can be matched with qualitative or safety information derived further down the marketing chain. This process will be expanded over time.

The third development, not as far along at this time, is the on-farm food safety initiative undertaken by AAFC in 2002. This concept is claimed to be designed strictly to assure food safety through the marketing chain. It is already in place on some livestock and poultry products, and is least developed in grains and oilseeds. The relevance is that it is a "traceback" process which provides a great deal of recorded on-farm information. It is therefore another form of IP which has its origins within the farm unit. Among these new initiatives, it is only the CGC that recognizes the relevance of their proposals to a common approach to IP in grains. The federal government has taken a rigid "food safety only" stance on their initiative and will not consider how that might coordinate with IP more generally.

There is no question that the CGC, which is responsible for quality assurance and certification of prairie grains, has recognized the need for IP facilitation, within and outside the application of genetically modified production. In that regard it appears to be ahead of much of the thinking among prairie grain regulators. At the same time, the private sector is also significantly involved in this evolution in grain handling.

Canadian Segregation and Identity Preservation Programs
There is a wide variety, and a long and growing history, of segregation and IP programs in the prairie grain industry. This section briefly reviews some of these programs in order to illustrate the array of crops and the variety of circumstances where segregation and IP has been used effectively.

Canadian Pedigree Seed Production and Distribution

Probably the oldest and most widely used varietal-IP system in Canada is the production and distribution of pedigreed seed. The Canadian Seed Growers Association, under the Canada Seeds Act, is responsible for establishing standards and issuing crop certificates on all agricultural product seeds, except potatoes. The regulatory process that exists for a crop like wheat is designed to assure genetic purity for each variety. According to the Canadian Seed Growers Association (CSGA) this IP system is the standard science-based seed reproduction process used around the world.[63]

This IP process has costs, including: field cleanliness, pure seed inputs, isolation strips, inspection, monitoring, certification, record keeping, and "clean machines." There are also upstream and downstream costs. The benefits side could be measured by the gross price difference between certified and common seed. In wheat, this price difference could be as little as fifteen percent of the seed costs, and as much as double in unusual cases (e.g., for new varieties) A twenty to thirty percent premium for certified seed over high quality wheat delivered to the elevator would likely be typical, but that gross margin has to cover cleaning, clean-out and other costs at the seed plant level.[64] New varieties often have plant breeders' fees built into the price as well but they should not be confused with IP costs for seed production and distribution.

Seed production and distribution have survived the market test over many decades in Canada and elsewhere, under very competitive market conditions. There is no shortage of independent seed growers despite the rapid growth over the past decade of large integrated seed producers/distributors in the business. Therefore, it can be concluded that observed margins are adequate to sustain the business. This evidence is relevant to the issue of IP on GM wheat in the following ways:

- seed wheat and non-seed wheat for food and feed use are often grown side by side on the same farms, using the same equipment, trucks, yard and storage facilities;
- the seed market supports the KVD process in wheat but seed production itself does not depend on KVD;
- knowledge, management, cleaning and care at the producer level, and standards established, administered and monitored by CSGA, are the drivers of this system;
- IP costs are significant, and price premiums are typically between 15 to 30 percent of the market price of wheat. Net price premiums are generally small because this is a genuinely competitive market;

- certification is a critical component of this IP system; and the entire system, in terms of assuring seed integrity and buyer confidence, has worked well for many decades.

High Acid Rapeseed (HAR)

The market for high quality industrial oil from rapeseed has grown since its contribution during WWII. Following the introduction of canola to replace rapeseed in the 1970s, "high acid rapeseed" became a niche market by the early 1980s. There are 100,000 to 150,000 acres of high acid rapeseed planted in Canada every year, much less than canola but still significant. Even though the acreage is relatively small, because the HAR is an industrial product in a food system, successful segregation is very important. At present high acid rapeseed is contracted across the prairies by one company which has oilseed processing facilities. A premium of $44/mt (or higher depending on conditions) fob the producer's bin is paid, seed is provided, fields are monitored by the buyer, and isolation strips are required. One reason for the large premium is the yield disadvantage of rapeseed compared to canola. This company carefully selects the growers who are offered contracts, and it depends to some degree on reliability of growers to assure integrity of the system.[65] Over the past two years 'grainfetti' has been used when binning the rapeseed.[66]

Canola and rapeseed are produced in the same areas, on the same farms, with the same equipment, stored in adjacent bins and company facilities, transported in the same trucks and crushed in the same plant. HAR is not visually distinguisable from most canola varieties. Canadian Food Inspection Agency (CFIA) regulations on this product are considered to be tighter than for most grains and oilseeds. This process has evolved over two decades and works well according to industry sources.[67]

B1602 Malting Barley.

As a consequence of widespread drought in the northern plains area in the United States in 1988, Anheuser-Busch made the decision to diversify its catchment area for malting barley into the Canadian prairies. It had a new variety, B1602, which had been tested in Canada and shown to perform well there. Saskatchewan Pool and Manitoba Pool elevator companies obtained "contract registration" rights on the seed stock in Canada, then set up producer contracts to supply Anheuser-Busch, providing the seed, selecting samples, facilitating arrangements through the CWB, and exporting the barley to the US company.

Selection of B-1602 was a sound business decision as it is still a major malting barley variety today, at least fifteen years later. It is used in Japan and by at least one major Canadian maltster. The grain handler provides seed stocks, has some field monitoring and conducts bin probes to confirm identity, but the real control in this process occurs as barley samples are submitted for acceptance. Carlot deliveries are used as in other malting barley deliveries.

The premium for B-1602, which is selected and sold as malt barley, is relatively large at present. On the 2002 and 2003 crops, and for the 2004 crop, the CWB paid or will pay a $10/mt premium on the initial price. In addition, Agricore United has offered an additional $5 or $10/mt premium on the initial price to encourage supply. This program therefore has returned $15-$20/mt premiums at the producer level, applied to the initial price, which means receipt on delivery instead of waiting for pool returns to be known. This is a substantial premium (relative importance comparable to HAR) which comes at small additional cost to producers or handlers[68] because malting barley generally is a small-lot, selected and segregated commodity.[69]

Canola (1995 and 1996)
In 1995 two seed companies had varieties of GM canola ready to be released for general production. IP systems were established for each variety which lasted to the end of the 1996 crop year while market testing was undertaken. These were detailed, tightly controlled systems involving a large number of players (a total of 9 seed developers, 5 elevator companies, 5 different processing plants, two chemical companies, and the Canola Council of Canada), with the objective of ensuring that the GM canola would not have any contact with the export channel. In other words, the market testing was done under conditions of zero tolerance for commingling with export shipments.

Using data from the Manitoba and Saskatchewan Pool elevators, Smyth and Phillips (2001) and Sparks Commodities identified the same five elements of cost increase from these programs, and provided *elevator company* estimates of those costs on the 1996 crop from 240,000 acres that were produced:

- on-farm costs (from separate storage requirements), $1/mt;
- extra transportation costs, $6.50-8.00/mt for one variety and $9.00-13.00/mt for the other;
- processor clean-out costs, $3.00-5.00/mt;
- IP coordination costs, $4.00-5.00/mt; and

- one elevator company estimated it would have lost the equivalent of $20.00/mt on this transaction because it would forego the revenue from handling other grain in order to deal in this canola (an imputed opportunity cost). A second company indicated its opportunity cost was $10.00/mt, with an additional $5.00 to $7.00 internal subsidy to the project.

The elevator companies therefore attributed costs of $33.00 to $41.00 per tonne for IP on these varieties in 1996. Sparks pointed out that producers probably received benefits from the new canola well in excess of the attributed $1per mt. of additional cost. In addition, Sparks suggested the elevator companies received benefits from increased volume from the project which were not accounted for.

These data provided by Smyth and Phillips (2001) and Sparks are not very helpful in allowing us to understand how an established IP system for canola (or any other crop) would function or what it would cost. First, the costs are likely inflated because of the large number of players and the amount of transportation involved. It may be understandable that these were necessary components of the canola test given the objectives at that time, but such a system for wheat, even in its early stages, would not have to involve so many players and should, therefore, be able to avoid a large share of these costs. Second, the analysis was incomplete in terms of cost components, which would imply full costs would have been even higher. For example, one dollar of extra costs at the farm level is likely low.

But the high "opportunity costs" supplied by the (Manitoba and Saskatchewan Pool) elevator companies, of $10 to $20/mt, were neither realized nor appropriate because, in a commercial system, the product would be handled only if it were commercially feasible. These data were used as an argument to not commercially segregate GM and non-GM canola and were, perhaps, presented in support of that outcome. Finally, clean-out costs and administration costs may have been reflective of this particular market test but are high in comparison to similar cost components in US segregation studies. Therefore, we do not learn much from this example because the estimates are not representative of credible IP system costs.

The Warburton Contract

Milling and baking firms in the United Kingdom supply products into markets that are highly differentiated in quality and price. Canadian and US wheat are important sources of high-end quality flour to blend with EU flour, and to produce the high-end, more expensive branded breads.

As mentioned in Chapter 2, in the late 1980s at least three new varieties (Katepwa, Roblin and Laura) registered in the high quality bread making class (CWRS) grew to represent a large proportion of the production of that wheat class on the Canadian prairies. Despite meeting the "equal-to-or-better-than-Neepawa" requirement for registration,[70] these varieties "lacked a certain synergy with the milling process in the UK."[71] The Canadian grading system was not able to identify and deliver the quality characteristics demanded by some major UK millers and bakers. As a result, Warburton set up a type of IP system to procure wheat varieties specific to its needs from the Canadian prairies.

The first commercial production and exports were made in 1995 and the program now represents a major portion of Canadian wheat exports to the UK. This IP program assures a package of qualitative characteristics, expressed in a blend of *three specific varieties*. The selection process now covers two *separated regions of production* (in the order of 200,000 acres), and *selection of individual growers*. There are two elevator companies that administer the program, from seed supply through to delivery into dedicated storage in terminals. Warburton has established a small testing laboratory in western Manitoba to do the same quality testing on post-harvest samples that are conducted pre-milling in the UK. The quality of contracted production is known by the producer, the elevator companies and the miller soon after harvest.

The two elevator companies do most of the administration, supply the seed, provide producer service and monitoring, and do the assembly, storage, shipping and in-Canada accounting. The elevator companies receive a special handling fee from the UK baker. The CWB receives a small fee (per mt) for facilitating the process. Producers sign a contract with one of the elevator companies, agree to meet a number of conditions required to ensure integrity of the IP system, submit samples after harvest and, if selected, deliver each variety in car lot amounts when called. For these services producers receive a $20/tonne (about 43 ¢/bu.) payment when the unload is certified as to quality at Thunder Bay. The Warburton grain is stored in dedicated bins at the port terminal by variety, then blended in specific proportions as it is loaded onto the vessel. The CGC certifies the cargo loaded onto the vessel at export.

This system is a comprehensive IP process that works on significant volumes and cargoes of wheat, from producers on farms across a wide expanse of the prairies to the mill in the UK. What is significant is that this is accomplished within the bulk facilities of the Canadian grain handling and transportation system, under the regulatory regime of the CWB including price pooling, to strict quality standards. The total return to all Canadian participants is a little less than $30 per mt (82 ¢/bu). The $20/mt premium to producers represents 10 to 15 percent on #2CWRS, 13.5 protein at recent on-farm prices.

Opponents to GM wheat argue that the Warburton example is not applicable as a model because rejected production from the Warburton program could go directly into the traditional system at a loss only of the $20/mt premium, whereas cargoes of wheat including GM wheat above tolerance could not. This argument misses the fact that there will always be the opportunity to blend lots of non-GM wheat down to tolerance, that there will be buyers who will be indifferent between GM wheat and traditional wheat, and that there will be buyers who will shift from non-GM to GM at a small discount. Then there is the feed market which is always available to wheat sales, but that is a last resort instead of opportunity value as some analysts argue.

The Warburton model, because it is an example of significant volume and acreage of wheat spread over two regions within the Canadian prairies, is highly relevant to the segregation of GM wheat. It provides the upper limit on what a system to keep separate GM wheat and conventional wheat would cost.

Soybeans
Soybeans are now part of the crop rotation of many producers in southern Manitoba. According to Manitoba Agriculture[72] there were around 50,000 acres in 2001, 125,000 in 2002, 220,000 in 2003, and an estimated 400,000 in 2004–about 82 percent were believed to be non-GM in 2003. At least three elevator companies and two seed/pulse dealers are buying these soybeans, with considerable involvement of Ontario non-GM dealers as well as a working relationship with the Ontario Bean Producers' Marketing Board. Manitoba soybeans are going to domestic crushers by rail cars, and some are going to the tofu market, a portion in containers. Producer deliveries are accepted in Manitoba outside of contracts because there is a high level of confidence in the test strip method of testing for GM material before unload (according to one of the companies buying those soybeans).

Because of the lack of GM soybeans in the province, the IP process with Manitoba soybeans is relatively simple, flexible and inexpensive. Elevator testing is estimated to cost no more than $1/mt and to be highly effective. The use of elevators that would otherwise be closed or dismantled suggests a net economic benefit from their use. Additional producer costs appear very low and there are no significant clean-out costs for producers because the only GM material on most farms is canola that would be removed in cleaning.

There is no hard evidence on the premiums or IP costs on soybeans in Manitoba. In 2001 the premiums in southern Manitoba were reported to be around 50 cents per bushel because of a short crop in Ontario. It was reported that in 2003 premiums were as high as 50 cents/bu. for premium number 2 soybeans destined for crushers, and as low as 10 cents, so there is considerable variation in the premium. Over the three years:

- acreage has expanded rapidly in Manitoba, mostly in non GM soybeans, and at premiums that are variable and in a range of 10 to 50 cents per bushel;
- one company is using old wooden elevators as dedicated receiving and storage facilities;
- contracting is being used but it has not been a necessary condition of marketing non-GM soybeans.

The Ontario soybean industry (like its counterpart in the US) has been sourcing, segregating and supplying variety specific, identity-preserved soybeans to the Asian market for at least fifteen years. These marketing programs pre-date the requirement to provide non-GM soybeans. As of 2001, the Canadian Soybean Export Association has an approved IP standard that producers and handlers are expected to follow in order to facilitate marketing, and to protect the integrity of Canadian (which really means Ontario) exports.

There are no publicly available estimates of IP costs for Ontario soybeans and efforts to collect estimates from dealers in Ontario met with confidentiality problems. We do know however that Ontario dealers, in collaboration with the Ontario Soybean Producers marketing board, have run a large and successful non-GM marketing program, including accessing the Japanese market, for over a decade. Manitoba soybeans form part of the Ontario exports because there are direct links between Manitoba and Ontario buyers.

CWB Contracts
In addition to its involvement in malting barley and the Warburton wheat contract, the CWB operates several variety-specific IP programs

each year as part of their market development initiatives. These programs involve contracts between the CWB and a producer, or a producer and an elevator company. These contracting programs have existed through the CWB for many years and are used on many different variations of wheat and barley production.

These programs go back to at least 1977 when a new promising barley variety (Beacon) was market tested. There have been several similar programs run on other barley varieties, CPS type wheats, at least two US wheat varieties, and more recently non-bread wheats. Most of these programs, but not all, are for relatively small volumes, are handled through the conventional elevator system, involve significant numbers of producers, and may or may not involve carlot deliveries. Not all varieties have met KVD standards. There are some instances of the contracting program being withdrawn with substantial amounts of grain, or seed, left in the system. Most of these programs require certified or higher quality seed, and require contracts that specify delivery, handling conditions and pricing factors. The contracts are promoted as having some added value besides the price premium such as full acceptance, early delivery or storage payments. Premiums are paid on contracted grain above the pool payment for the same or similar class. A summary of some illustrative CWB contract programs is provided in Table 3.1.

The price premia data from CWB contracts are interesting in the context of a segregation or IP program in GM wheat even though they do not provide information on what it costs to IP in wheat at the farm or marketing level. The CWB programs indicate that a relatively small premium and minor secondary benefits such as favorable delivery conditions and payment for storage will induce IP of wheat at the producer level. Navigator wheat contracting requirements are met with a $2.50/mt cash premium to producers. Other typical cash premiums are $5/mt and $7.50/mt to producers. Industry sources suggest that seed sales on proprietary varieties may be enough inducement for elevator companies to undertake the additional handling costs, while small handling charges, less than $2/mt may be negotiated with the CWB.

Compared with the Warburton contracts, the financial and secondary benefits combined are much smaller on these CWB contracts while the IP conditions are not much less constraining on the grower.

Conclusions From Existing IP and Segregation Programs
The important conclusion emerging from this analysis is that segregation

Table 3.1. Summary of CWB IP Programs, 2002-2004

Program	Contract	KVD	Seed/Isolation	Field Inspection/ Other	Post Harvest [All Sampled and Called Up if Selected]	Costs	Premium to Producer	Comments
AC Vista (SPSW) 2002 (terminated 2003)	Yes	-	(S) Yes, Proprietary	No	One Company	Unknown, small	$5/mt	Delivery Assurances Premium<Marketing Costs
AC Navigator (XSCWAD) 2002-2004	Yes	No	(S) Yes, Proprietary	No	One Company	Unknown, small	$2.50/mt	Delivery Assurances Storage Payments
5700PR (CPSR)	Yes	-	(S) Yes, Proprietary (IS) No	No	One Company	Unknown, small	$5/mt	Delivery Assurances Storage Payments Protein Premiums
Snowbird/Kanata (CWEHWW) 2003-2004	Yes	Yes	(S) Yes, Proprietary (IS) No	No	One Company	Unknown, small	$7.50/mt> CWRS initial	Delivery Assurances Storage Payments
Hard Red Winter Wheat (CWRWSW)	Yes	Yes	(S) No (IS) No	No, >11.5% Protein	All Companies	Unknown, Small	$10/mt	Delivery Assurances Storage Payments

Source: CWB *Grain Matters* and website, various dates.

Table 3.2. Illustrative Prairie Non-CWB Segregation and IP Programs

PROGRAM (Dates)	Contract(C)/ Regulations (R)/ Other	KVD	Seed (S)/ Isolation Strips (IS)	Monitoring/ Field Inspection/ Other (O)	Post Farm Handling/ Transport	COSTS Farmer (F) Other (O)	Premium Farm (F) Other (O)	Comments
Pedigree Seed (decades)	Canada Seeds Act (R)	No	(S) yes (IS) yes	M, FI paper trail	n.a.	(F) Ave. costs < benefits (sustained)	(F) variable about 15-30%	Viable, long standing grain market
Oats (since 1989)	C/NC elevator/dealer processor	Some, but not important	(S) no (IS) no	No	Bulk	(F) Almost none	(F) < 10%	Purchased by contract specs
High Acid Rapeseed (since 1980)	Processor (C)	No	(S) yes (IS) yes	Some, use grainfetti at storage	Direct to processor	(F) Some lost yield, less than prem.	(F) $40 to $50/mt	Must be kept separate
B1602 Malting Barley (since 1988)	Elevador (C) [CWB]	Partly, but not a factor	(S) yes (IS) no	Some M, FI, post harvest sample	Carlot delivery	(F) Small	(F)$10+/mt CWB & elevator	Larger premium paid in '03 and '04
RR Canola 1995 & 1996	(experimental) (C)	No	(S) yes (IS) yes		Direct to processor	(F) Small (O) $5 to $50/mt	(O) pooled costs	Outdated
Warburton Wheat (since 1996)	Farm to elevator Warburton (C)	No	(S) yes variety specific (IS) no	Binning post harvest & delivery sample	Carlots special binning throughout	Less than $30/mt all costs	(F)$20/mt (O) about $10/mt	Variety specific & non-KVD
Non GM soybeans/ Manitoba (since 2001)	Contract and walk-up deliveries	Some: varieties only	(S) non-GM (IS) no	Some (on contract)	On-truck tests some dedicated elevators	Very small	(F) 10 to 80 ¢ per bu. over 2 years	Manitoba is a new producer

Source: Interviews with grain industry officials.

problems should not be a deterrent to introduction of GM wheat in Canada. There are many examples of successful, long-standing and new segregation and IP programs operating on the prairies. They vary in complexity, in contract conditions, in premiums paid, and cover a wide array of commodities. Tables 3.1 and 3.2 summarize the important features of several of these IP systems.

The Warburton model is a good example to build on in wheat, although the level of non-GM price premiums at the producer level may not be required if either CWB contracts or malting barley are used as an indicator of the dollar amount per acre required to provide incentives for producer participation. What is lacking from this overview of prairie IP segregation systems are costs and returns after producers have placed their commodities into the marketing system.

Estimated Cost of a GM Wheat IP/Segregation Program
What would be the cost of avoiding the commingling of GM and non-GM Canadian wheat throughout the marketing chain? From the literature and foregoing discussion, it would appear that there are many variables that determine the cost to segregate and/or IP grains. There are costs related to system design and logistics, such as common, shared, or designated facilities; side-by-side or sequenced use; relative volumes of the products to be segregated; and whether or not the system is capable of handling only bulk commodities by traditional bulk handling methods. There are another set of costs that arise from institutional characteristics of the market such as the tolerance levels for non-prescribed grains in the sample; the penalty for failure to meet the tolerances; and liability and costs of correcting a mistake picked up subsequent to delivery to a customer.

Then there are transactions costs incurred to assure integrity of the IP system: monitoring, in the sense of following commodity development (quality control in a manufacturing context); testing at critical market junctures; providing for a risk premium if required; and compiling the evidence and information to be able to certify a sale. Finally, cutting across all of these areas are physical issues of cleaning equipment and facilities, and providing extra facilities for storage and handling if those are required. In order to properly identify segregation and IP costs and feasibility, a particular model relevant to the particular commodity and circumstances needs to be specified.

The GM wheat issue has generated a number of detailed economic studies by academics in the United States. For Canada, neither a serious literature search nor direct communication with parties involved in the IP and GM wheat debate have produced evidence of any thorough economic or business analysis of the feasibility or costs of IP systems in relation to wheat on the Canadian prairies beyond a Masters level thesis at the University of Saskatchewan (Gosnell). The Canada Grains Council produced estimates of IP costs for "bulk grain shipments" (Canada Grains Council 2003), collected from elevator companies,[73] apparently without any economic analysis, and for a report to Mexico to convince that country not to apply certain regulations on imports. That evidence, like the data provided in the 1996 Sparks Commodity report, does not provide useable cost estimates for our purposes.

Recognizing that there has been little useful analysis of GM wheat segregation systems conducted in Canada, we will attempt to synthesize available information. We rely heavily on the more complete US evidence, and on Gosnell.

Canadian Studies
Gosnell synthesized (private and regional) segregation costs of GM wheat, under different production and handling conditions in a specific region in south central Manitoba. The region represented about 2.7 million acres of cropland with slightly less than one million acres in wheat; it was assumed that GM and non-GM wheat would be produced and marketed in the region. Nine large inland terminals handled all the production from the region within a transportation-cost minimization model, and high-throughput elevators were assumed to turn 12.86 times per year at rates below (then) current handling charges. He simulated segregation costs for the following scenarios:

- three handling options: one designated high throughput elevator (HTP) handling only non-GM wheat and other commodities, multiple (re-opened) designated smaller wooden elevators across the region operated by one firm, and segregation only within the HTP elevators;[74]
- three adoption rates of GM wheat by farmers within the region, at 20, 50 and 80 percent of the acreage;
- three levels of demand for non-GM wheat, at 60, 120 and 180 thousand mt. or 2.4, 4.8 and 7.2 million bushels respectively; and
- testing costs were pegged at $8/load for a 40 tonne load based upon strip tests but against a tolerance level of 0.5% for GM presence, at a 99% confidence level.

Each of the combinations of these variables had cost scenarios generated under the assumption that "tolerance levels are such that segregation is feasible," costs represented those required to load cars for shipment out of the region, and without contamination risk[75] directly factored in (Gosnell, p.4). In principle, this array of conditions is consistent with the type of analysis that is required to provide useable information on segregation costs in a GM wheat environment. At the outset, the only assumption that may be too restrictive is the 0.5% tolerance for GM material in conventional wheat but that is somewhat offset by lack of a risk factor.

The Gosnell base case scenario produced $43.15 per mt. average transportation and handling costs to move grain out of the region, and simulations were assessed according to additional segregation costs above the base. The lowest costs generated by his simulations were associated with high volumes moving through high-throughput elevators with segregated handling. Segregation cost estimates ranged from less than $2/mt (large demand, low adoption rate) to about $5.60/mt (all demand levels, 80% adoption rate). At 50% adoption rate and all levels of demand, costs were very similar at $2.75 to $2.95/mt. However, when Gosnell applied ex-post risk analysis to costs (at a loss of up to $85/mt on contaminated wheat sales as feed), the risk cost of commingling (ranging from $2.92/mt to $99.17/mt) overtook the lower handling costs. On this basis, Gosnell rejected segregation in terminals as a feasible option. Our conclusion is that his risk premiums were excessive. He ignores the fact that in most markets for non-GM crops, if there were accidental commingling, then the wheat could be blended down to meet the tolerance level or sold into a non-feed GM wheat market.

Multiple points using wooden structures were the most expensive option in the Gosnell analysis. The lowest simulated costs for multiple points through wooden structures was $13.72/mt at low volumes, and the highest were between $17.00 and 18.95/mt at 80% adoption rate.

Considering commingling risks, a designated high-throughput elevator produced the lowest cost option, ranging from $3.54/mt (9.6 ¢/bu.) to $8.36/mt (22.7 ¢/bu.) at 50% adoption, and $6.85/mt (18.6¢/bu.) to $14.68 (40¢/bu.) for an 80% adoption.

The simulated results reinforce what other studies have shown on the responsiveness of costs to adoption rate and volume of movement, and while this risk analysis appears to be too conservative, it is clear that assumptions about commingling costs and probabilities, and salvage value can reverse results. Gosnell notes the significance of achieving multiple car discounts in the economics of handling wheat. This study is a useful template for considering a comprehensive IP/segregation system for wheat on the prairies.

Huygen, Veeman, and Lerohl provide a recent (2003) estimate of the likely costs of segregating non-GM from GM wheat. They assume that about 50% of CWRS exports would be non-GM, and they find that identity preservation of non-GM in this setting:

(1) is relatively low cost in terms of some of the conventional wisdom on this issue; and
(2) is more costly for lower tolerance levels

Their estimates of segregation costs are about 50% higher than ours because they did not model a sequenced delivery system and they include a "coordination" cost with little explanation. Huygen, Veeman and Lerohl attribute about one-half of their total estimated IP costs to fixed "coordination" costs ($3.75 per mt) which appear very high. Their total estimated costs are $6.71/mt (18¢/bus), $6.73 (18¢/bus), and $8.26 (22¢/bus) for 5%, 3% and 1% tolerance, respectively. We believe that if their results were refined to a sequenced "call-up" model, then their cost estimates would be lower and in line with our estimates.

US Studies
Wilson and colleagues have conducted several useful analyses of biotech crops in the grain handling and transportation system (Wilson, Jabs and Dahl, Wilson et al., Dahl and Wilson). One of the observations which has been repeated in Wilson's work is that the nature of the Canadian production and handling system implies that IP of wheat in a GM/non-GM era will be easier than in the United States because there is already significant varietal segregation in the Canadian system. Had some form of declaration system been introduced as the CGC proposed in early 2003, the case for the Wilson proposition would have been even stronger.

Wilson et al. (January 2003, p.40) provide a tabular summary of IP and segregation costs on several commodities, by different analysts and different estimation techniques. As usual in economic analysis with this many variables, the range of estimates is huge, 1 to 72 US cents per bushel or, in Canadian dollars, about 55 cents to forty dollars per tonne.[76] Table 3.3 provides a few specific examples.

Table 3.3. Previous Studies on IP and Segregation Costs

Researchers	Description	Costs
Hurburgh, et al. 1994	Cost accounting/High Oil soybeans	3.7 ¢/bu.
Nelson, et al. 1999	Survey Grain Handlers/soybeans	18 ¢/bu.
Bullock, et al. 2000	Cost Accounting/soybeans	30-40 ¢/bu.
Dahl and Wilson, 2002	Survey	25-50 ¢/bu.
Wilson and Dahl, 2001	Survey elevator mgrs/wheat	15 ¢/bu.

Source: Wilson, Janzen, Dahl and Wachenheim.

This list could also include Wisner, who recognized lower estimates of 4 US cents per bushel for segregation, up to a USDA estimate of 70 US cents per bushel when domestic and overseas costs plus producer premiums were included.

Another contribution from the United States is Wilhelm (2003). That study involved simulation analysis on cost structures of segregating wheat in country elevators of different sizes and organization in the eastern half of the state of South Dakota. In some respects it provides comparable elevator costs information to the Gosnell thesis (except for the regional dimension of Gosnell's study). Wilhelm's testing costs (elevator only, using strip tests) ranged from 1.2 US cents per bushel to 1.4 US cents per bushel for 1% tolerance at the 99% confidence level. His overall elevator costs for segregation ranged from 1.3 US cents to 16.4 US cents per bushel and were highly sensitive to the opportunity cost of unused capacity within a segregation regime (Wilhelm, p. 81). One elevator in his sample had costs that were twice as large as the next highest, because it had large bins that were underutilized and had high opportunity costs. Dropping this observation from the sample (say, assuming the regime was applied only where opportunity costs could be held down by higher utilization rates), then the overall estimated elevator costs fell within a narrower range of 1.3 to 8.8 US cents per bushel. In Canadian dollars, that translates to 64 cents to just over $4 per tonne which is comparable to the segregation-in-terminals estimates that Gosnell produced.

These studies provide some information that can be applied to our task, but they also indicate that estimating segregation and IP costs is very case-specific. Wilson et al (January 2003, p.xi) provide some conclusions that are a useful overview to segregation issues and costs:

- strip testing procedures are being developed for wheat that should produce costs of 0.2 to 3.6 US cents/bu. using 2001 testing technology (in Canadian terms, the average would be 92 cents per tonne); and

- risk of rejection if buyer tolerance is exceeded is a real cost in an IP program.

Wilson estimated a 1.75% rejection rate with reasonable monitoring and testing within his modeling of the wheat in the northern plains wheat marketing system (Wilson et al., January 2003; p.43) that translated into

- a cost of about 3-4 US cents per bushel if all costs were attributed to the non-GM product. These costs included all testing costs at the elevator (every fifth car) and terminal (PCR), and rejection costs under his set of assumptions. In Canadian dollars, that translates to $1.66/mt; and
- his estimates assumed a varietal declaration system. In the absence of such a system, the testing costs quadrupled.

This is where the Canadian system has an advantage over the US system. There is varietal segregation in Canada, and in terms of wheat, CWB call-ups provide a larger measure of programmed deliveries, as opposed to producer or elevator determination of when wheat is delivered. In addition, we will see below that, in Canada, ISO elevators already do some clean-out between product runs, and samples are taken and retained on every producer delivery and every car or truck loaded out of the elevator. These are strict, voluntary monitoring and control mechanisms already in place in the ISO operations.

Projecting Segregation Costs
All of the forgoing discussion indicates that IP estimates range widely, that they are dependent on certain assumptions like testing costs, tolerance levels and capacity utilization, and that the particular model of IP heavily influences the results.

We begin by assuming that GM wheat has penetrated the market to the seventy percent level and the IP task is to preserve the identity of the thirty percent of production that is conventional HRS wheat. That would imply about 7.0 million acres of conventional wheat and about 6.0 mmt of production. Without further information, we also assume that GM wheat would become a weed control crop, and non-GM wheat would be a rotational crop dependent on the price spread between GM wheat and non-GM wheat. The assumptions imply more acreage and production than any existing IP programs have achieved to date in Canada, but the proportions are similar to those that exist in canola. Like canola, we assume production is widespread, and not concentrated in particular areas.

Previous economic analyses, which has been done on IP programs, indicates a distinct payoff to using "designated facilities" as long as those facilities can be used near capacity. We know that the Warburton model works well, and the malting barley and CWB contracts based on "call-up" procedures accomplish the functions required of them. As a result, we adopt a model that reflects all of these strategies. We assume the IP system will involve wheat being assembled, handled and transported through the bulk handling system in a "sequenced" manner similar to the present practice of "runs" of grain through high throughput facilities. In other words, "call-ups" of non-GM wheat would be used to assemble, receive and load out trains of identity preserved or segregated non-GM wheat. This model is a variation of "designated facilities" in which a particular facility is designated to handle a particular product.

"Designation" in this model means allocating certain time slots to the IP crop and keeping any product that may risk contamination out of that facility until the "run" is completed. It is not much different from the way the CWB now handles contract calls, where prior notification of the call is given, there is high volume over a short time-period, and there is an expiry date. Interestingly, in this limited context, this might be argued to be a benefit of the regulatory process applied in assembling prairie grain. The transportation logistics are set up to match train runs to handle these calls. Similarly, high throughput elevators use this method of assembling grain (oats, canola, wheat, soybeans) for achieving the multiple car discounts available from the railways.[77] Instead of bearing constant risk of mixing GM and non-GM wheat in a side-by-side operation, this procedure would limit risk to a short time frame and require clean-out only two to four times a year depending on the volume and timing of calls. The approach combines the segregation-in-inland terminals advantage, and avoids some of the disadvantages of fully designated facilities, reported by Gosnell. We will call this method of special designated handling the "call-up" IP procedure.[78]

Our assumption is that the typical call-up would be four 50-car trains. Most HTP elevators on the prairies can handle 50-car trains today, thus achieving a significant multiple car rate discount, in the order of $3.50/mt. To handle 6 mmt of production of non-GM wheat by the call-up IP method would require about 350 50-car trains. Some HTPs could assemble and load out two or three trains per week, others may manage only one per week, the difference depending on storage space, car availability and producer willingness to deliver. Under these conditions, it appears reasonable to argue that two, three or four call-ups at a particular point would accommodate the non-GM market. Some HTP elevators may choose not to participate in the program. In any event, the "call-up" IP model does not, to this stage of specification, require anything that is not already being done within the HTP elevators or CWB procedures for assembling wheat.

The literature illustrates very clearly that the opportunity cost of unused elevator capacity is an important cost factor in some IP scenarios. Almost all the HTP elevators on the prairies are creations of the last decade with similar design and component size. Larger elevators are achieved by replicating components. A 1,600-mt bin is a typical size and represents about 18 cars of shipment. Unlike the US system that has many sizes and configurations of elevators built over a much longer period of time, prairie high-throughput elevators are much more homogeneous, particularly in storage components. In view of the similarity of our model to existing programs in the prairie grain industry, and the similarity of elevators serving 50 car trains, it is reasonable to argue that the issue of unused capacity should not arise, and there should not be significant opportunity costs associated with unused capacity in the call-up IP system.

The next step is to specify the testing method and regime. We assume that wheat test strips will be available when required, that three strips per truckload (and rail car) are adequate at the receiving and shipping levels of country elevators, and that strips would be used at terminal unload, while PCR testing would be used onto vessel. The test strips would detect GM wheat in a non-GM truck or rail car. So our model assumes three sets of test strips (at $2.50/strip) and one application of the DNA polymerase chain reaction (PCR) test at the vessel. The Canadian handling system, for those elevators that are part of Hazard Analysis Critical Control Points (HACCP) and International Organization for Standardization (ISO) conventions, now undertake activities that reduce the cost of additional GM testing. First, all deliveries to, and shipments from, ISO operations have samples taken and stored for up to 90 days. These samples are taken on every individual delivery to the elevator and every individual car or truck loaded out by the facility. That means that testing costs do not include sampling costs, which probably represent up to half the labor component of most estimates of testing costs. Our analysis uses a combination of the Gosnell and Wilhelm assumptions to estimate these costs, adjusted for these considerations. Their analyses purported to assure meeting tolerance of 0.5% or 1% within 99% confidence intervals. For a variety of reasons the results we produce are almost certainly overestimates of costs that would be realized in practice, particularly since GM testing technology is a rapidly developing area of science and costs are coming down.

Based on interviews with operators of HACCP and ISO compatible elevators, our model assumes that each elevator will have to be cleaned before there is a call-up of IP wheat, and a cost estimate is provided for this scenario.[79] ISO certification means that all the loading equipment in HTP elevators is cleaned after use and before more grain is shipped, for both rail cars and trucks that are loaded. This means that only the leg, boot and bins need to receive additional cleaning. We received an estimate of about $250 for these tasks, which included four 1,600 mt bins, enough for more than a 50 car train. The extra cost is, therefore, only 4 cents per mt if the operation is following HACCP rules. Doubling or tripling these costs have little meaningful impact on overall costs. The existence of HACCP procedures and ISO certification substantially reduces the additional work that is required for an IP program, and therefore the costs.

Assuming HACCP/ISO protocols, the costs of running an effective IP system according to our "call-up" proposal should be able to achieve both lower cost and more effective segregation, which translates into lower risk of contamination (and another cost reduction) than any of the analyses that have been conducted and reviewed in this study. That is because:

- the "call up" system, with or without contracting, is only a small departure from the way much of the grain is now assembled for shipping runs on the prairies, therefore;
- cost of unused storage and handling facilities should be small or eliminated;
- HACCP/ISO protocols already accomplish much of what would be required to sample and clean facilities for IP wheat;
- with every HTP unload and load-out sampled, the one-in-five car rule of testing used by several analysts to limit risk of contamination in rail cars becomes a one-for-one rule, thereby further reducing risk of error and imputed risk cost. In HACCP eligible facilities every unload and load-out is sampled and the sample is retained; and
- test strip technology is reported to be moving ahead at a rapid pace, implying that strip costs will come down. Combined with the situation of population evidence in HACCP/ISO elevators on the prairie, sampling, testing and risk costs should be reduced over time.

Wilson et al., estimated these risk costs at $1.66/mt. We use reduced estimates relative to Wilson, first of $1/mt and then 50 percent of Wilson's estimate.

Table 3.4 summarizes the imputed IP costs under these assumptions. The largest cost component is the special binning costs in the terminals. Testing costs are very small at all levels in the handling and transport system. Because of the particular characteristics of our model and the prairie HTP system under HACCP/ISO protocols, the risk cost is also low.

Table 3.4 Estimated Costs of Segregating GM from non-GM CWRS with up to 75% GM Wheat Adoption

Level	Function	Cost	Cost/mt	Comments
Farmer	strip test 3 strips per load 0.5% tolerance @ 99% confidence	$12.50/load overstated includes sampling cost	32¢/mt to $1.25/mt average $0.50/mt	test strips @$2.50 each are the major cost. High estimate; costs will fall.
HTP elevator "call up"	clean leg, boot, 4-1600 mt bins before deliveries;		< 5 ¢/mt	HACCP elevators already clean other components;
	strip testing before loading cards	$7.50/car	8-9 ¢/mt	sampling is already done on every car.
Transport	check and clean dirty cars	av. $2/car	2 ¢/mt	one in 4 cars cleaned @ ½ hours
Terminal	test unloads		8-9 ¢/mt	same as loading except for labor cost. Upper limit.
	Special binning		$1-2 / mt	Low end of Canada Grains Council estimate
To vessel	Test		5-25 ¢/mt	PCR test @ $250 on 1000 to 5000 mt lots
	Certify		0	
Total			$1.83-3.05/mt	**3.6 - 8.3 cents/ bu.**
Add Wilson risk factor	@ $1/tonne		$2.83-4.05/mt	**7.7- 11 cents/ bu.**
	@ 50% of Wilson= 85 cents/tonne		$2.68-3.90/mt	**7.2- 10.6 cents/ bu.**

Source: Estimated from literature reviews, industry sources, and inference from available data.

Our estimates of total testing costs range from $2.68/mt to $4.05/mt (see Table 3.4) in Canadian dollars and are consistent with costs reported in several other studies with one important exception–the top of the range is much lower because sampling is already done in HACCP/ISO facilities. Furthermore, part of the terminal and country elevator cleaning would be done in HACCP/ISO plants.

Conclusions

In the Canadian context, the CWB and others have claimed that the cost to segregate GM and non-GM wheat is so prohibitive (up to $1 per bushel) that it makes no sense to commercialize GM wheat. In this chapter we investigate this claim and find that it is indefensible. In fact, there is a long and growing history with a wide variety of segregation and IP programs in the prairie grain industry. For instance the Warburton bakery in the U.K. has set up a very successful identity preservation type system to procure wheat varieties specific to its needs from the Canadian prairies. The Warburton model provides the upper limit on what a system to keep separate GM wheat and conventional wheat would cost.

We provide cost estimates of segregating non-GM wheat in a bulk handling system with GM wheat for production levels of GM wheat exceeding fifty percent of total wheat acreage on the prairies. We assume the IP system will involve wheat being assembled, handled and transported through the bulk handling system in a "sequenced" manner similar to the present practice of "runs" of grain through high throughput facilities. The cost of segregation in Canada under this type of system would be approximately 7 to 11¢ per bushel.

4. GM WHEAT'S POTENTIAL ECONOMIC VALUE TO GROWERS AND THE INDUSTRY

Using field trial, market, and cost of production data, this chapter estimates the impact on financial returns to the typical prairie farmer from adopting GM wheat compared to conventional wheat varieties, under a standard crop rotation. The industry wide economic effects are also estimated. We are interested in the following questions: What are the farmgate economic implications of the main agronomic benefits of GM wheat such as increased yield, reduced chemical costs, etc.? How do crop rotations affect the potential benefits and how much variability in returns is there across major soil zones on the Canadian prairies? What is the breakeven point for farmers on the price of GM wheat seed and the technology fee? What are the industry wide economic implications of widespread adoption of GM wheat in western Canada? What if Canada does not adopt biotech wheat but competitors in the world market do adopt?

Our research has the following major findings:

- There are large potential farm level benefits associated with adoption of biotech wheat. The estimated gains associated with adopting GM wheat range from approximately $4 to over $24 per acre, after growers pay a technology fee of $7 per acre.
- Using the option value approach recommended by the Grain Industry Working Group on Roundup Ready® wheat and employed by Furtan, Gray and Holzman (2003b), we find there is significant gain to the industry from immediate adoption of GM wheat of approximately $280 million per year.
- Using a simulation model of the world wheat market, global economic gains from commercialization of GM wheat are estimated to be $3.9 billion per annum (USD), of which Canada gains approximately $140 million per year.

Background
In order to estimate the farm-level net economic benefits associated with the adoption of GM wheat on the Canadian prairies, this chapter uses a static, partial budgeting approach. Economic estimates were developed based on average cost and herbicide application figures and assuming standard crop rotations. The prairie provincial governments produce detailed cost and return studies for wheat, including rotations. For example, see the Alberta Agriculture website.[80] In this chapter we utilize these

cost studies and build on the previous work by Holzman. As in Holzman, we focus on changes in yields, returns, and chemical and seed costs per acre resulting from GM wheat adoption.

Potential producer benefits were estimated by calculating net returns over operating costs, based on representative growers in each of the three main soil zones on the prairies: brown, dark brown and black. Sensitivity analysis was then undertaken to account for the heterogeneity in growing conditions across the prairies, as well as uncertainty regarding yields, and the technology fee. The interactions among GM wheat and other crops in a typical rotation are accounted for. Our results suggest that a management strategy including Roundup Ready® varieties could lead to significant economic benefits for the grower and the industry, as well as benefit the environment.

The brown soil zone is primarily in southern Saskatchewan and southern Alberta (see Table 4.1). This area is very dry; annual precipitation averages 340 mm, and soil organic matter is lower than in the other two zones that we consider. Typical farming patterns in the brown soil zone include crop-fallow rotations. The dark brown soils are adjacent to the brown soils and lie to the north of the brown zone. Rainfall is higher in the dark brown region (averaging 370 mm per year), and soil organic matter is also higher than the brown zone. The crops grown in the dark brown zone are mainly wheat and other small grains. The black soils are in southern Manitoba and the northern agricultural areas of Saskatchewan and Alberta. Soil organic matter and precipitation are higher in this region and a wider variety of crops are grown including wheat, coarse grains, oilseeds, peas, and specialty crops.

Table 4.1. Soil Zones of Western Canada: Cultivated Acres

Soil Zone	Manitoba	Saskatchewan	Alberta	Total
TOTAL (million acres)	11.1	45.1	24.2	80.4
Share of Acreage (%)				
Brown	-	25%	17%	19%
Dark Brown	-	35%	19%	25%
Black	77%	30%	19%	25%
Dark Grey	14%	8%	16%	11%
Grey Luvisol	9%	2%	9%	6%
TOTAL	100%	100%	100%	100%

Source: *Prairie Land and Water - The Last 100 Years* (http://collections.ic.gc.ca/soilandwater/index.htm

The primary direct effects of biotech wheat adoption on the cost structure of prairie farmers are:

- reduced herbicide and application (including fuel, labor, and machinery) costs; and
- increased costs due to a technology fee; and
- increased yield due to improved weed control.

In addition, biotech wheat has the potential to simplify overall weed management strategies, through decreasing the amount and number of chemicals applied to a particular field. The cost impact on growers will be ultimately determined by the degree of substitutability (in terms of effectiveness) among herbicides and the relative chemical prices. Similarly, savings in herbicide application costs per acre depend on the specific chemical(s) involved and the means of application.

For this chapter, we estimate changes in overall costs. As mentioned above, the adoption of GM wheat is unlikely to significantly change farm overhead expenses and several other cost items associated with growing wheat. The exception is additional costs due to the need to keep GM wheat segregated from conventional wheat on the farm, which will have additional costs. Except for these additional activities, management practices and costs are assumed unchanged with the adoption of GM wheat compared to conventional wheat. In other words, we assume that the costs of management, fertilizer, fuel, insurance, etc. are the same whether GM or conventional wheat is grown. This means that our estimates of the benefits of adoption are conservative, because we do not account for any reduced management costs associated with growing GM wheat.[81] In other words, our simplification of the cost impact of GM wheat means that we understate the cost savings to growers associated with moving from conventional to GM wheat.

In addition to generating cost savings, cultivation of GM wheat may also affect revenue per acre due to:

- higher yields;
- reduced dockage;
- reduction in crop injury due to chemicals;
- ability to seed an earlier crop; and
- ability to use a non-selective herbicide (i.e., Roundup®) that controls broadleaf and grassy weeds with just one application.

GM wheat will help prevent yield losses arising from weed infestation. As such, potential yield gains resulting from the adoption of GM wheat are dependent on the existing degree of weed problems and the effectiveness of chemical treatment, so there will be variation in impact from farm to farm. Many adopters of transgenic corn, cotton, canola, and soybeans have experienced positive yield effects (Marra, et al., Gianessi, et. al., McBride and Brooks; Fernandez-Cornejo and McBride), and of course net returns to the farmer will be positively correlated with the yield improvements.

Another impact of commercialization of biotech wheat on prairie growers' returns is the potential development of price premia for conventional wheat varieties in domestic and world markets. There is demand uncertainty in world grain markets, especially in the European Union (EU) and Japan, with regard to GM crops. Although challenged by the major GM crop producing countries (the United States, Argentina, and Canada), the EU has restricted imports of new GM crops. Many other importers have varying GM crop threshold labeling regulations including China, Japan, the Republic of Korea, the Russian Federation, and Thailand (Carter and Gruere 2003a, Foster, Berry and Hogan). As such, these regulations have the potential to ensure there is some demand for non-GM wheat. Due to segregation requirements and the higher unit cost of producing non-GM wheat, this introduces the potential for a price premium for non-GM wheat. Such premiums have developed in markets for non-GM corn and soybeans.

As a result, non-adopters of GM wheat on the Canadian prairies may indirectly benefit from the introduction of GM wheat.

Estimating Farm Level Benefits
Model Overview
Our model of farm-level benefits builds solidly on the work of Holzman, and contains many of his assumptions. Wherever possible, we maintain the Holzman assumptions (such as for herbicide costs) so that our results can be directly compared, and the differences easily seen. When our assumptions differ (such as for the increased yield and technology costs of RR wheat) we discuss the differences. The main extensions of Holzman that we introduce include:

- a stochastic analysis of changing parameter values, while Holzman confined his study to a deterministic analysis;
- economic estimates of adoption benefits for three soil zones, while Holzman assumed one soil zone.

Holzman performed a farm-level analysis of the economic benefits of adopting Roundup Ready® wheat and Clearfield® wheat.[82] He estimated the benefits of adopting the herbicide-tolerant varieties both on a stand-alone basis, and as part of a crop rotation. The crop rotation assumed by Holzman was a wheat-canola-barley-peas cycle. In year one, he assumed that the farmer has a choice of three alternative wheat systems: conventional, Roundup Ready®, or Clearfield® wheat. In year two, the farmer chooses from three alternative canola systems: conventional, Roundup Ready®, or Clearfield®. Barley and peas are grown in each Holzman rotation during years three and four.

The wheat-canola-barley-peas rotation used by Holzman is particularly appropriate for the black soil zone, and we adopt it in this study as well. Because canola follows wheat in this rotation, estimates of farm level benefits throughout the rotation must consider herbicide-tolerant varieties of canola, as well. Holzman includes conventional canola, Roundup Ready® canola and Clearfield® canola in his analysis. The interaction between herbicide-tolerant wheat and herbicide-tolerant canola is particularly important in back-to-back years in a rotation. We use Holzman's assumptions regarding applied herbicides for all possible crops in the standard rotation. An exception is that we consider a rotation with genetically modified Liberty Link® canola, which Holzman does not analyze.

We extend Holzman's work in developing a model for the black soil zone, although our assumptions are somewhat different. As shown in Table 4.2, our estimate of the yield benefit associated with Roundup Ready® wheat is higher than Holzman's (9% instead of his 6%), and our technology fee is substantially lower ($7 per acre rather than his $15 per acre). Our technology fee assumption is based on discussions with industry experts. It approximates the fees in other genetically modified crops, like Roundup Ready® soybeans and Roundup Ready® corn, as a percentage of the seed costs (Annou, Wailes, and Cramer). Our assumption of a 9% yield premium for of Roundup Ready® wheat is based on the only published reports of actual field trials for Roundup Ready® wheat: Blackshaw and Harker, and Kidnie et al. both report Canadian field trial results which show mean yield gains of a least 9%. Holzman uses a 6% yield premium for both RR wheat and Clearfield wheat as a baseline, with a range of 2-10% in his analysis. Furtan, Gray and Holzman (2003b) have a most likely increase in yields from adopting RR wheat of 3%, basing their estimate on Holzman and the opinion of crop scientists.

Table 4.2: Key Assumptions Compared to the Holzman Study

	Holzman	Carter, Berwald & Loyns
Yield Advantage of GM wheat	2–10% (base = 6%)	3-13% (base = 9%)
TUA ($/acre)	$15	$7
Conventional Wheat Price Premium[83]	$5-20/acre (17 to 68¢ per bu.)	15¢ per bu.

There are two important differences between our model of the black soil zone and Holzman's. The first is that Holzman estimates the benefits of rotations based on Clearfield® wheat, and we do not include Clearfield® wheat in our analysis. Unlike Holzman, we are focusing on genetically modified (GM) wheat rather than generic herbicide-tolerant (HT) wheat, so we do not include Clearfield® wheat among our possible rotations. Including Clearfield® wheat would give the grower alternative rotational options and more flexibility for weed control. Second, we include a price difference between conventional wheat and GM wheat. We believe that after an initial transition period, non-GM wheat will be segregated from Roundup Ready® wheat, and that most of the world market will accept GM wheat. Some markets will pay a premium for non-GM wheat, so we model the price impact of GM wheat as a price premium for conventional (i.e., non-GM) wheat, rather than a price discount for GM wheat. As indicated above, there is ample evidence of price premia for both non-GM soybeans and non-GM corn in the Japanese and EU markets, and elsewhere. In order to capture this price premium, GM wheat will be segregated at the farm level, and we include additional costs for GM wheat producers reflecting additional segregation costs.

We also expand on Holzman's work by considering the adoption of GM wheat in two other soil zones. We adopt Holzman's rotation for the black soil zone, but develop separate rotations for the brown and dark brown soil zones, because the agronomic conditions are different from zone to zone.

In the brown soil zone, the baseline rotation that we use is conventional wheat-fallow-durum-fallow, and the rotation with Roundup Ready® wheat is Roundup Ready® wheat-fallow-Roundup Ready® wheat-fallow. In the dark brown soil zones, the baseline rotation is conventional wheat-flax-canary seed-lentils, and the rotation that we model with GM wheat is Roundup Ready® wheat-flax-canary seed-lentils. More detail on herbicide use for each soil zone is given below.

We use these rotations for the purpose of showing the effect of biotech wheat on costs that occur after harvest, typically for controlling volunteer wheat in subsequent crops. These four-year fixed rotations simplify the reality that farmers do not plant farms cut up into three or four blocks, they plant fields, and the number of fields on a typical prairie farm far exceeds the number of crops. Furthermore, the crops are not uniformly distributed over the fields. This is important because the number of combinations available in a rotation (to control the adverse impacts of using GM or any other technology) increase in relation to the product of the number of crops and number of fields. Rotational constraints limit this outcome but typically by less than either the number of fields or crops. This means that instead of the four combinations in the rotation analysis that we develop, the number of possible combinations is large, and so are the opportunities to manage problems. This is a more flexible picture than the four year fixed rotation analysis we are using here; it means that for any particular GM crop, there are many follow-up crops and agronomic solutions for controlling volunteers. The actual combination of crops that can be used in any rotation varies by location, soil type, moisture conditions and market opportunities but they are manyfold greater than the simple four crop rotations illustrated here.

Biotech wheat and other genetically modified crops provide additional flexibility to the prairie growers. Additional flexibility may be quite valuable, but we do not attempt to estimate its value here. Even within our simplistic four-year rotations we minimize the management flexibility in order to ensure that our estimates of net benefits are conservative. We do this by substituting GM for conventional wheat in the rotation, but not allowing other crops to change. For example, in the black soil zone, in rotation with Roundup Ready canola, we assume that Roundup Ready® wheat is substituted for conventional wheat, and no other changes are made. On an actual field, the decision to plant Roundup Ready® might be made at the same time as the decision to switch to another herbicide-tolerant canola, to avoid planting two Roundup Ready® crops back to back.

Methods
This study uses a partial budgeting approach to estimate changes in net returns over operating costs for the average wheat farmer on the Canadian prairies, who adopts transgenic wheat. This type of approach has been used in a variety of previous economic studies for a number of transgenic crops (Fulton and Keyowski; Annou, Wailes, and Cramer; Holzman; Gianessi, et al.; and Alston, et al.). In addition to the basic analysis, we provide sensitivity analysis by varying yields and technology fees using deterministic assumptions, as well as using Monte Carlo methods to represent the stochastic nature of yields and output prices. Most previous studies of the economics of GM crops have not provided this type of sensitivity analysis.

To illustrate our approach, let π_i represent per acre returns over operating costs for the ith technology (i = conventional (C) or genetically modified (GM)). Specifically, let:

$$\pi_i = (P_i - c)Y_i - FC - SC - HC_i - TUA \quad (4.1)$$

where P_i is the farm-level price of type i wheat, c is the marginal harvest cost per acre for either variety, Y_i is the per acre yield of the ith wheat, FC is fixed costs per acre, SC is the seed cost for both conventional and GM wheat, and HC_i, is chemical costs per acre for the ith wheat, and TUA is the technology fee for using GM seed. Another possible cost to consider is the on-farm costs of keeping GM and non-GM wheat separate. We do not include these costs in our model, because we think that the adoption of Roundup Ready wheat would be widespread among most producers, who would sell into the large market that will accept GM wheat. Producers who do not adopt GM wheat are assumed to grow non-GM wheat on their entire acreage, so they have no additional costs. Subtracting returns for conventional wheat production from those for GM wheat and rearranging, we obtain:

$$(\pi_{GM} - \pi_C) = (P_{GM} - c)(Y_{GM} - Y_C) - (P_C - P_{GM})Y_C - (HC_{GM} - HC_C) - TUA \quad (4.2)$$

Equation (4.2) illustrates each of the potential adoption impacts on the net returns to the grower. The $(P_{GM} - c)(Y_{GM} - Y_C)$ term on the right-hand side is the yield effect: the value of adopting GM wheat solely due to increased yield. The second term on the right-hand side $(P_C - P_{GM})Y_C$ is an opportunity cost to adopting GM wheat: the "lost" increase in revenue from not receiving the non-GM price premium. The remaining terms in the equation are the cost effects of the technology: $(HC_{GM} - HC_C)$ is the difference in herbicide costs, which will be negative (so beneficial to the grower) if herbicide costs are lower with GM wheat. The seed costs disappear from equation (4.2) because we assume they are the same for GM and conventional wheat.

To help illustrate our results, we first set the potential yield gain, price premium, and additional seed costs to zero, as in Annou, Wailes, and Cramer, so that only the effects of herbicide costs (including application costs) are initially captured. These results provide a base estimate of the economic rents associated with the introduction of GM wheat. We then use two distinct methods in order to perform sensitivity analysis. First, we relax the assumptions of zero yield and seed cost effects by deterministically varying the yields of the GM variety and the technology fee. This provides a range of per acre grower benefits in the presence of hetero-geneity, as we suspect that eventual adopters tend to have relatively greater weed problems, while other farmers with fewer weed problems may experience little or no yield advantage.

The second approach is to specify probability distributions for the key variables in Equation (4.2), and use Monte Carlo simulation analysis in order to obtain an empirical distribution of the estimated benefits of the new technology. Unlike the deterministic analysis in most previous studies, we identify GM wheat yield (Y_{GM}), price of GM wheat (P_{GM}), and the price premium of conventional wheat over transgenic wheat ($P_C - P_{GM}$) as stochastic variables, assume likely distributions, and take 10,000 draws from these distributions in order to estimate a confidence interval for the change in per acre net returns from adoption, in the presence of uncertainty.

Assumptions.
This section provides detail on the assumptions we used to estimate the net economic benefits of adopting GM wheat.

Table 4.3: Rotations by Soil Zone

Black
a. Conventional wheat-conventional canola-barley-peas (baseline)
b. Roundup Ready® wheat-conventional canola-barley-peas
c. Conventional wheat-Roundup Ready® canola-barley-peas (baseline)
d. Roundup Ready® wheat-Roundup Ready® canola-barley-peas
e. Conventional wheat-Clearfield® canola-barley-peas (baseline)
f. Roundup Ready® wheat-Clearfield® canola-barley-peas
g. Conventional wheat-Liberty Link® canola-barley-peas (baseline)
h. Roundup Ready® wheat-Liberty Link® canola-barley-peas

Dark Brown

a. Conventional wheat-flax-canary seed-lentils (baseline)
b. Roundup Ready® wheat- flax-canary seed-lentils

Brown

a. Conventional wheat-fallow-durum-fallow (baseline)
b. Roundup Ready® wheat-fallow-durum-wheat-fallow

Rotations

The net benefits of adopting GM wheat for a single year are given by equation 4.2. We also consider the net benefits of adopting GM wheat in a four-year rotation for three different soil zones. The rotations for each soil zone are listed in Table 4.3. The estimated net economic benefits in a four-year rotation represent the difference between the present value of net returns over a four year period with GM wheat in the rotation minus the present value of returns from what is labeled the "baseline" rotation in parentheses in Table 4.3.

For the black soil zone, there are four baseline rotations with conventional (non-GM) spring wheat: conventional wheat-canola-barley-peas, where the canola is conventional, Roundup Ready®, Clearfield® or Liberty Link® canola respectively. The substitution of Roundup Ready® wheat for conventional wheat is the only change we make when calculating the benefits for the different types of canola.

In the dark brown soil zone, the baseline rotation is conventional (non-GM) spring wheat-flax-canary seed-lentils. When Roundup Ready® wheat is adopted; it replaces conventional wheat in the rotation.

In the brown soil zone, the baseline rotation is conventional (non-GM) spring wheat-fallow-durum-fallow. In this zone, when Roundup Ready® wheat is adopted, it replaces both conventional wheat and durum in the rotation, and the rotation becomes Roundup Ready® wheat-fallow-Roundup Ready® wheat-fallow.

Applied Herbicides. To a large extent, the change in costs of production from adopting biotech wheat depends on the total cost of herbicides applied to the conventional crop. Table 4.4 lists the herbicides that are used for each crop in each four-year rotation, for both conventional and low-disturbance tillage regimes. For the Roundup Ready® crops, the herbicide is listed as "Roundup," but a technology fee is also paid by the grower. In the case of the black soil zone, we use the herbicide application mix identified by Holzman for each rotation, so that our results will be comparable to his. Two important changes from Holzman's analysis are: 1) the pre-seed treatments for low-disturbance tillage apply to only 80% of the grower's acreage, because not all of the acreage needs weed control every year; and 2) for the Roundup Ready® crops, we use only one treatment of Roundup® with low-disturbance tillage, rather than the two treatments assumed by Holzman, based on information from industry experts.

Table 4.4: Black Soil Zone Herbicide Use Assumptions

Year	Crop	Herbicide Use with Low-Disturbance Tillage
1	Conventional Wheat	Roundup (Pre-Seed), Harmony Total
2	Conventional Canola	Roundup (Pre-Seed), Muster Gold, Pre-Harvest Roundup
3	Barley	Roundup (Pre-Seed), Puma + Buctril
4	Peas	Roundup (Pre-Seed), Odyssey
1	Roundup Ready® Wheat	Roundup
2	Conventional Canola	Roundup + Assure (Pre-Seed), Muster Gold, Pre-Harvest Roundup
3	Barley	Roundup (Pre-Seed), Puma + Buctril
4	Peas	Roundup (Pre-Seed), Odyssey
1	Roundup Ready® Wheat	Roundup
2	Roundup Ready® Canola	Roundup + Assure
3	Barley	Roundup + 2,4-D (Pre-Seed), Puma + Buctril
4	Peas	Roundup (Pre-Seed), Odyssey
1	Roundup Ready® Wheat	Roundup
2	Clearfield® Canola	Roundup + Assure (Pre-Seed), Odyssey, Pre-Harvest Roundup
3	Barley	Roundup (Pre-Seed), Puma + Buctril
4	Peas	Roundup (Pre-Seed), Odyssey
1	Roundup Ready® Wheat	Roundup
2	Liberty Link® Canola	Roundup (Pre-Seed) + Assure, Liberty + Select, Liberty
3	Barley	Roundup (Pre-Seed), Puma + Buctril
4	Peas	Roundup (Pre-Seed), Odyssey

Year	Crop	Herbicide Use with Low-Disturbance Tillage
1	Conventional Wheat	Harmony Total
2	Conventional Canola	Muster Gold, Pre-Harvest Roundup
3	Barley	Puma + Buctril
4	Peas	Odyssey
1	Roundup Ready® Wheat	Roundup
2	Conventional Canola	Muster Gold, Pre-Harvest Roundup
3	Barley	Puma + Buctril
4	Peas	Odyssey
1	Roundup Ready® Wheat	Roundup
2	Roundup Ready® Canola	Roundup + Assure
3	Barley	Puma + Buctril
4	Peas	Odyssey

Table 4.4. (Continued)

1	Roundup Ready® Wheat	Roundup
2	Clearfield® Canola	Odyssey, Pre-Harvest Roundup
3	Barley	Puma + Buctril
4	Peas	Odyssey
1	Roundup Ready® Wheat	Harmony Total
2	Liberty Link® Canola	Liberty + Select, Liberty
3	Barley	Puma + Buctril
4	Peas	Odyssey

Source: Adapted from Holzman, and Manitoba Guide to Crop Protection, 2003.

Table 4.5 shows the herbicides applied for the two rotations in the dark brown soil zone, for both conventional and low-disturbance tillage regimes. This table is different from Table 4.4 because Roundup is applied at three different rates: 0.85 liters/acre (the baseline), 1 liter per acre, or 0.5 liters per acre. In some cases, treatments are repeated, as reported in the table. As in the black soil zone, 80% of the low-disturbance acreage is given a pre-seed treatment of Roundup, either alone or in a tank mix with 2,4-D or Assure. For conventional wheat, the final treatment is a 1 liter per acre treatment of Roundup for controlling perennial weeds. Not all land needs this control every year, and we assume that only 20% of the acreage planted to conventional wheat is treated. The table also reports tillage treatments when the land is fallow, but there is no herbicide cost associated with tillage. Tillage without an applied herbicide is reported in the table for a full reporting of all weed control measures, although the cost of tillage is not estimated in our analysis.

Our assumptions regarding the herbicides applied to the brown soil zone are reported in Table 4.6. The rotations in this zone allow Roundup Ready® wheat to replace both conventional wheat and durum, separated by a year of fallow.

The herbicide cost savings of Roundup Ready® technology are clearly an important part of the farm-level impacts. The costs per acre of Roundup and other herbicides used are reported in Table 4.7. For the black soil zone, we based our analysis on Holzman, but some of our assumptions regarding herbicide costs and use are different from Holzman's. In particular, our cost of Roundup used "in-crop" is higher than Holzman, $6.80 per acre compared to his $4.30 per acre. This is because we make two different assumptions about the cost and use of Roundup. First, our assumed cost of Roundup is $8.00 per liter, compared to Holzman's $8.60 per liter. On the other hand, we assume a higher application rate of 0.85 liters per acre, compared to Holzman's 0.5 liters per acre. Roundup is also used with low-disturbance tillage as a pre-seed treatment. As above, Holzman assumes the cost is $4.30 per acre, and we assume a higher cost of $6.80 (because of the higher application rate) per acre. We assume that only 80% of the acreage is given a pre-seed treatment. This gives us a per acre cost of Roundup pre-seed treatment in a low-disturbance tillage regime a cost of $5.44 per acre.

Assure is used to control volunteer Roundup Ready® crops both as a pre-seed treatment with low-disturbance tillage, and for in-crop control. We modeled the pre-seed treatment differently than Holzman. We assumed a higher cost of treatment ($4.94 per acre), but only applied that treatment to 80% of the acreage, which gives us the same overall cost ($3.95 per acre). However, for control in Roundup Ready® canola following Roundup Ready® wheat, our cost estimates for Assure are much higher than Holzman. He assumes a cost of $4.13 per acre,[84] and we assume double that cost, or $8.26 per acre.

Table 4.5: Dark Brown Soil Zone Herbicide Use Assumptions

Year	Crop	Herbicide Use with Low-Disturbance Tillage
1	Conventional Wheat	Roundup (pre-seed) .5L/Acre, Horizon + Refine Extra, Roundup 1L/Acre
2	Flax	Roundup 0.5L/Acre (pre-seed), Poast Ultra + Lontrel + MCPA
3	Canary Seed	Avadex MicroActive, Buctril M
4	Lentils	Edge, Sencore + Poast Ultra, Reglone
1	Roundup Ready® Wheat	Roundup, 0.5L/Acre, 2 Treatments
2	Flax	Poast Ultra + Lontrel + MCPA
3	Canary Seed	Avadex MicroActive, Buctril M
4	Lentils	Edge, Sencore + Poast Ultra, Reglone
Year	Crop	Herbicide Use with Low-Disturbance Tillage
1	Conventional Wheat	Horizon, Refine Extra, Roundup 1L/Acre
2	Flax	Poast Ultra + Lontrel + MCPA
3	Canary Seed	Avadex MicroActive, Buctril M
4	Lentils	Edge, Sencore + Poast Ultra, Reglone
1	Roundup Ready® Wheat	Roundup, 0.5L/Acre, 2 Treatments, TUA
2	Flax	Poast Ultra + Lontrel + MCPA
3	Canary Seed	Avadex MicroActive, Buctril M
4	Lentils	Edge, Sencore + Poast Ultra, Reglone

Table 4.6: Brown Soil Zone Herbicide Use Assumptions

Year	Crop	Herbicide Use with Low-Disturbance Tillage
1	Conventional Wheat Dyvel DS	Roundup 0.5L/acre (pre-seed), Horizon,
2	Fallow	Rustler 1L/Acre, 2 Treatments; 1 Tillage Treatment
3	Durum Wheat	Roundup 0.5L/acre (pre-seed), Spectrum
4	Fallow	Rustler 1L/Acre, 2 Treatments; 1 Tillage Treatment
1	Roundup Ready® Wheat	Roundup, 0.5L/Acre, 2 Treatments, tech. fee
2	Fallow	Roundup 0.5L/Acre + Assure, 2 Treatments, 1 Tillage Treatment
3	Durum Wheat	Roundup 0.5L/acre (pre-seed), Spectrum
4	Fallow	Roundup 0.5L/Acre + Assure, 2 Treatments, 1 Tillage Treatment

Year	Crop	Herbicide Use with Low-Disturbance Tillage
1	Conventional Wheat	Horizon, Dyvel DS
2	Fallow	3 Tillage Treatments
3	Durum Wheat	Spectrum, Roundup 1L/acre
4	Fallow	3 Tillage Treatments
1	Roundup Ready® Wheat	Roundup, 0.5L/Acre, 2 Treatments, tech. fee
2	Fallow	3 Tillage Treatments
3	Durum Wheat	Spectrum, Roundup 1L/acre
4	Fallow	3 Tillage Treatments

Table 4.7: Herbicide Cost Assumptions

Herbicide Treatments	Cost ($/acre)
Avadex MicroActiv	11.04
Buctril	5.76
Dyvel DS	4.61
Edge	14.69
Everest	13.42
Harmony	20.75
Horizon	13.77
Libèrty	13.70
Lontrel	24.63
MCPA	2.12
Muster Gold	20.98
Odyssey	23.00
Poast Ultra	20.00
Puma + Buctril	20.20
Refine Extra	5.21
Roundup, In Crop (0.85 L/acre)	6.80
Rustler	5.95
Select	10.75
Sencor	10.00
Spectrum	11.34

Zero-Tillage Treatments, Pre-Seed, $/acre

Roundup (same as above)	6.80
Roundup, 0.5L/acre	4.00
Roundup, 1.0L/acre	8.00
Percent of Zero-Till Producers Roundup for pre-seed	80%
2,4-D (in mix w/ Roundup)	2.00
Assure (in mix w/ Roundup for Volunteer Control)	4.94
Percent of Zero-Till Producers using Assure (Black and Brown Soil Zones)	80%

Volunteer RR Wheat Control in Subsequent RR Crop, $/acre

In-Crop Assure (in mix w/ Roundup)	8.26
Percent of Producers using Assure	100%
Pre-Harvest treatment for Clearfield® and Conventional Canola (1L/acre)	6.80

Sources: Holzman, Manitoba Agriculture, Food, and Rural Initiatives.

In the other soil zones, we assume different application rates for Roundup, as listed in the tables above, either 0.5 liters per acre or 1 liter per acre, or the baseline of 0.85 liters per acre.

In these cases, the cost of the herbicide is adjusted, based on the assumed cost of $8.00 per liter. In the brown soil zone, conventional spring and durum wheat under low-disturbance tillage gets a pre-seed treatment of Roundup at 0.5L/acre, but that treatment is applied to only 80% of the acreage. Roundup Ready® wheat is given two treatments of Roundup at a concentration of 0.5L/acre, and the treatments are applied to all the acreage. In the Roundup Ready® rotation, the fields are left fallow the year after Roundup Ready® wheat is planted. With low-disturbance tillage, the fallow field is given two treatments of a tank mix of Roundup and Assure, and one tillage treatment. The herbicides are again assumed to be applied to 80% of the acreage. For the dark brown soil zone, under low-disturbance tillage, both conventional wheat and flax get a pre-seed treatment of Roundup at 0.5L/acre, which is assumed to be applied to 80% of the acreage. With both conventional and low-disturbance tillage, non-GM wheat is listed as getting a treatment of Roundup at 1L/acre. This is for perennial control, and it is assumed to be needed on only 20% of the acreage

In these cases, the cost of the herbicide is adjusted, based on the assumed cost of $8.00 per liter. In the brown soil zone, conventional spring and durum wheat under low-disturbance tillage gets a pre-seed treatment of Roundup at 0.5L/acre, but that treatment is applied to only 80% of the acreage. Roundup Ready® wheat is given two treatments of Roundup at a concentration of 0.5L/acre, and the treatments are applied to all the acreage. In the Roundup Ready® rotation, the fields are left fallow the year after Roundup Ready® wheat is planted. With low-disturbance tillage, the fallow field is given two treatments of a tank mix of Roundup and Assure, and one tillage treatment. The herbicides are again assumed to be applied to 80% of the acreage. For the dark brown soil zone, under low-disturbance tillage, both conventional wheat and flax get a pre-seed treatment of Roundup at 0.5L/acre, which is assumed to be applied to 80% of the acreage. With both conventional and low-disturbance tillage, non-GM wheat is listed as getting a treatment of Roundup at 1L/acre. This is for perennial control, and it is assumed to be needed on only 20% of the acreage.

Finally, the other necessary baseline assumptions we made are reported in Table 4.8. This table lists all of the critical assumptions regarding yields, seed costs, and prices. Where possible, these assumptions are taken from Holzman, to keep our results comparable. For crops not used in Holzman's

Table 4.8: Parameter Assumptions

Expected Crop Price ($/bu)

Conventional Wheat	$4.15
Roundup Ready® Wheat	4.00
Roundup Ready® Canola	7.05
Clearfield® Canola	7.05
Liberty Link® Canola	7.05
Conventional Canola	7.05
Barley	2.20
Lentils	0.18 ($/lb.)
Flax	7.50
Canary Seed	0.15 ($/lb.)
Durum	4.25
Fallow	0.00

Expected Yield (bu/ac)

Conventional Wheat	29.60
Roundup Ready® Wheat	32.26
Conventional Canola	21.90
Roundup Ready® Canola	24.09
Clearfield® Canola	24.09
Liberty Link® Canola	24.09
Barley	48.80
Lentils	1,100.00 (lb./acre)
Flax	23.00
Canary Seed	1,165.00 (lb./acre)
Durum	30.00
Fallow	0.00

Total Seed Costs ($/acre)

Conventional Wheat	$12.38
Roundup Ready® Wheat	12.38
Conventional Canola	12.90
Roundup Ready® Canola	19.20
Clearfield® Canola	19.20
Liberty Link® Canola	19.20
Barley	7.88
Lentils	13.50
Flax	7.35
Canary Seed	8.05
Durum	12.38
Fallow	0.00

Technology Fee for Roundup Ready® wheat ($/acre)	$7.00
Discount Rate	8%

Sources: Holzman, Saskatchewan Agriculture, Food, and Rural Revitalization.

analysis, the figures are based on crop protection handbooks provided by provincial governments, and farm management data in the Saskatchewan Crop Planning Guides. We maintain assumptions such as yield across different soil zones constant, in order to keep our analysis simple. The price for conventional wheat is assumed to be $4.15 per bushel, a price premium of 15 cents per bushel over Roundup Ready® wheat. The yield for conventional wheat is 29.6 bushels per acre, and the yield for Roundup Ready® wheat is 32.26 bushels per acre, representing our base assumption of a 9% yield increase. The Roundup Ready® wheat yield of 32.26 bushels per acre is our baseline; we vary it in the analysis below. Our baseline technology fee is $7 per acre, lower than Holzman's $15 per acre, but we allow the technology fee to vary in our analysis below, as well. The $7 technology fee assumption is based on discussions with industry experts, and it is also consistent with the technology fee used in other Roundup Ready® crops. Using Roundup Ready® corn and soybeans, a single-gene technology currently on the market, as a reference point, the technology fee is approximately thirty to sixty percent of conventional seed costs per acre (Annou, Wailes, and Cramer). This would put the technology fee for wheat in a range of approximately $4 to $7.50 per acre.

Modeling Results
We report results for a range of estimated biotech wheat yield benefits. For more detailed results, including different assumptions for the technology fee, and descriptions of how the results were obtained, see the following section.

Single-Year Benefits. Table 4.9 presents the single-year per-acre benefits of adopting Roundup Ready® wheat in each of the three soil zones. These estimates ignore any rotational considerations, and simply consider the net benefits of growing Roundup Ready® wheat in place of conventional wheat. The benefits reported in Table 4.9 are comparable to what Holzman refers to as "static benefits." Reduced herbicide costs and increased yields over conventional wheat are the source of these single-year benefits from adopting Roundup Ready® wheat.

These figures account for the technology fee charged for the use of Roundup Ready® seed, and the foregone price premium captured by those growers producing conventional wheat. In Table 4.9, net benefits are reported for alternative levels of yield increases for Roundup Ready® wheat. Based on field trial results published by Blackshaw and Harker, and Kidnie et al., we believe that a yield increase of 9% is the most plausible outcome, but we present results for a range of yield increases from 3% to 13%. Even at the low end of this range, farm-level benefits from the adoption of Roundup Ready® wheat are significant, due to lower herbicide costs.

Table 4.9: Estimated Single-Year Net Benefits of Roundup Ready® Wheat ($/acre)

Yield Benefit from Roundup Ready® Wheat	Black Soil Zone		Dark Brown Soil Zone		Brown Soil Zone	
	Low-Disturbance Tillage	Conventional Tillage	Low-Disturbance Tillage	Conventional Tillage	Low-Disturbance Tillage	Conventional Tillage
3%	$11.50	$6.06	$7.89	$4.69	$5.69	$2.49
5%	$13.87	$8.43	$10.26	$7.06	$8.06	$4.86
7%	$16.24	$10.80	$12.63	$9.43	$10.43	$7.23
9%	$18.61	$13.17	$15.00	$11.80	$12.80	$9.60
11%	$20.97	$15.53	$17.36	$14.16	$15.16	$11.96
13%	$23.34	$17.90	$19.73	$16.53	$17.53	$14.33

Table 4.10: Discounted Benefits of Roundup Ready® Wheat in Rotation with Conventional Crops ($ per acre)

Yield Benefit from Roundup Ready® Wheat	Black Soil Zone		Dark Brown Soil Zone		Brown Soil Zone	
	Low-Disturbance Tillage	Conventional Tillage	Low-Disturbance Tillage	Conventional Tillage	Low-Disturbance Tillage	Conventional Tillage
3%	$11.50	$6.06	$10.85	$4.69	$1.56	$2.49
5%	$10.21	$8.43	$13.22	$7.06	$3.93	$4.86
7%	$12.58	$10.80	$15.59	$9.43	$6.30	$7.23
9%	$14.95	$13.17	$17.96	$11.80	$8.67	$9.60
11%	$17.32	$15.53	$20.33	$14.16	$11.04	$11.96
13%	$19.68	$17.90	$22.69	$16.53	$13.40	$14.33

The estimated benefits reported in Table 4.9 range from a low value of $2.49 per acre with an assumed yield increase of only 3% in the brown soil zone, to a high value of over $23.00 for a 13% yield increase in the black soil zone with low-disturbance tillage. In general, the highest estimated benefits are in the black soil zone, and the benefits are lowest in the brown soil zone. At our baseline 9% yield increase from GM wheat we expect the farm-level benefits to adoption in the range of $9.60 to $18.61 per acre (shown in bold in the center row of Table 4.9).

Benefits within a Rotation. Wheat is typically grown in rotation with other crops on the Canadian prairies, and Table 4.10 reports the present value of net benefits from adopting biotech wheat over a four-year rotation with conventional crops, in each of the three soil zones. In Table 4.10, net benefits are reported for the same range of yield increases over conventional wheat that are reported for the single year benefits in Table 4.9. As in Table 4.9, the benefits reported in Table 4.10 are calculated for growers using both low-disturbance tillage and conventional tillage techniques.[85]

The estimated net benefits (reported in Table 4.10) over the whole four-year rotation are lower than the estimated single-year benefits reported in Table 4.9. This is because there are additional costs to controlling volunteer Roundup Ready® wheat in following years. However, the estimated benefits are still positive at all levels of assumed yield increases. For the most likely 9% yield gain, the estimated grower benefits range from $8.67 to over $17.96 per acre.

Herbicide-tolerant canola is presently grown on a large scale in Canada, and if it is in the same rotation as Roundup Ready® wheat, the benefits to Roundup Ready® wheat may be smaller. Roundup Ready® canola accounts for about 50% of the prairie canola acreage, Liberty Link® for about 25%, and Clearfield® for about 15%. The rotations we model in the brown and dark brown zones do not include canola, so this is only an issue in the black soil zone. Table 4.11 reports the results of adopting Roundup Ready® wheat in a rotation that includes herbicide-tolerant canola. In this table, the benefits of Roundup Ready® wheat are calculated assuming the canola crop does not change; we are not allowing substitute choices of canola if Roundup Ready® wheat is adopted. When Roundup Ready® wheat is adopted in rotation with Roundup Ready® canola, with low-disturbance tillage the estimated benefits are all positive, ranging from $6.22 to $15.69 per acre. With conventional tillage in rotation with Roundup Ready® canola, the estimated benefits are negative for growers who might

Table 4.11: Discounted Net Benefits of Roundup Ready® Wheat-HT Canola Rotation in the Black Zone ($ per acre)

Yield Benefit from Roundup Ready® Wheat	Rotation with Roundup Ready® Canola		Rotation with Clearfield® Canola		Rotation with Liberty Link® Canola	
	Low-Disturbance Tillage	Conventional Tillage	Low-Disturbance Tillage	Conventional Tillage	Low-Disturbance Tillage	Conventional Tillage
3%	$3.85	($1.59)	$7.84	$6.06	$7.84	$6.06
5%	$6.22	$0.78	$10.21	$8.43	$10.21	$8.43
7%	$8.59	$3.15	$12.58	$10.80	$12.58	$10.80
9%	$10.96	$5.52	$14.95	$13.17	$14.95	$13.17
11%	$13.33	$7.89	$17.32	$15.53	$17.32	$15.53
13%	$15.69	$10.25	$19.68	$17.90	$19.68	$17.90

expect a very low Roundup Ready® wheat yield increase of 3% (a loss of only $1.59 per acre). As yield gains from Roundup Ready® wheat relative to non-GM wheat increase, the economic benefits of Roundup Ready® wheat adoption increase, and they range up to $10.25 per acre, with conventional tillage. In rotation with Clearfield® and Liberty Link® canola, the benefits of Roundup Ready® wheat are positive for all levels of yield increase, ranging from $8.43 per acre to about $19.68 per acre.

Sensitivity Analysis. In this section we present more detailed tables on how the farm-level benefits of adopting biotech wheat depend on the yield increase and the technology fee assumed in the model. In the tables below, a range of values for the GM wheat yield increase for over conventional wheat (from 3% to 13%) is presented, as well as a range of values for the technology fee paid by producers (from $3 to $11 per acre). Our baseline numbers are in the highlighted row and column of each table for ready comparison. As expected, farm-level benefits are higher with higher yield increases and lower technology fees. For the black soil zone, the detailed modeling results are presented in Table 4.12. The first panel of the table, labeled "Single-Year: Low-Disturbance Tillage," shows the estimated farm-level impact of adopting Roundup Ready® wheat over conventional wheat using low-disturbance tillage, but without accounting for rotational considerations. The benefit estimates range from a low of $7.50 per acre to a high estimate of $27.34 per acre, and they are all positive. The benefits of adoption using conventional tillage are given in the second panel of Table 4.12. The estimates range from a low of $2.06 to a high estimate of $21.90 per acre.

Table 4.12, also presents the farm-level benefits of adopting GM wheat as part of a four-year rotation, as described in Table 4.9 above. The rotations all follow the pattern of wheat-canola-barley-peas. The numbers in Table 4.12 represent the farm-level benefits of adopting biotech wheat in the place of conventional wheat in the rotation. The benefits to adoption as part of a four-year rotation depend on the canola crop that follows the GM wheat in the second year of the rotation. We present results for conventional canola, Roundup Ready® canola, herbicide-tolerant Clearfield® and Liberty Link® canola, considering both conventional and low-disturbance tillage The farm-level benefits are lowest, in general, in rotation with Roundup Ready® canola, due to the extra cost of controlling volunteer glyphosate-tolerant wheat in the following year's canola crop.

Table 4.12. Farm-Level Benefits of Adopting GM Wheat in the Black Soil Zone

Single-Year			Low-Disturbance Tillage		
			Tech Fee ($/Acre)		
	$3	$5	$7	$9	$11
Increase in Yield					
3%	$15.50	$13.50	**$11.50**	$9.50	$7.50
5%	$17.87	$15.87	**$13.87**	$11.87	$9.87
7%	$20.24	$18.24	**$16.24**	$14.24	$12.24
9%	**$22.61**	**$20.61**	**$18.61**	**$16.61**	**$14.61**
11%	$24.97	$22.97	**$20.97**	$18.97	$16.97
13%	$27.34	$25.34	**$23.34**	$21.34	$19.34

Single-Year			Conventional Tillage		
			Tech Fee ($/Acre)		
	$3	$5	$7	$9	$11
Increase in Yield					
3%	$10.06	$8.06	**$6.06**	$4.06	$2.06
5%	$12.43	$10.43	**$8.43**	$6.43	$4.43
7%	$14.80	$12.80	**$10.80**	$8.80	$6.80
9%	**$17.17**	**$15.17**	**$13.17**	**$11.17**	**$9.17**
11%	$19.53	$17.53	**$15.53**	$13.53	$11.53
13%	$21.90	$19.90	**$17.90**	$15.90	$13.90

Rotation with Conventional Canola			Low-Disturbance Tillage		
			Tech Fee ($/Acre)		
	$3	$5	$7	$9	$11
Increase in Yield					
3%	$11.84	$9.84	**$7.84**	$5.84	$3.84
5%	$14.21	$12.21	**$10.21**	$8.21	$6.21
7%	$14.80	$12.80	**$10.80**	$8.80	$6.80
9%	**$18.95**	**$16.95**	**$14.95**	**$12.95**	**$10.95**
11%	$21.32	$19.32	**$17.32**	$15.32	$13.32
13%	$23.68	$21.68	**$19.68**	$17.68	$15.68

Table 4.12. (Continued)

Rotation with Conventional Canola		Conventional Tillage			
		Tech Fee ($/Acre)			
	$3	$5	$7	$9	$11
Increase in Yield					
3%	$10.06	$8.06	**$6.06**	$4.06	$2.06
5%	$12.43	$10.43	**$8.43**	$6.43	$4.43
7%	$14.80	$12.80	**$10.80**	$8.80	$6.80
9%	**$17.17**	**$15.17**	**$13.17**	**$11.17**	**$9.17**
11%	$19.53	$17.53	**$15.53**	$13.53	$11.53
13%	$21.90	$19.90	**$17.90**	$15.90	$13.90

Rotation with RR Canola		Low-Disturbance Tillage			
		Tech Fee ($/Acre)			
	$3	$5	$7	$9	$11
Increase in Yield					
3%	$7.85	$5.85	**$3.85**	$1.85	($0.15)
5%	$10.22	$8.22	**$6.22**	$4.22	$2.22
7%	$12.59	$10.59	**$8.59**	$6.59	$4.59
9%	**$14.96**	**$12.96**	**$10.96**	**$8.96**	**$6.96**
11%	$17.33	$15.33	**$13.33**	$11.33	$9.33
13%	$19.69	$17.69	**$15.69**	$13.69	$11.69

Rotation with RR Canola		Conventional Tillage			
		Tech Fee ($/Acre)			
	$3	$5	$7	$9	$11
Increase in Yield					
3%	$2.41	$0.41	**($1.59)**	($3.59)	($5.59)
5%	$4.78	$2.78	**$0.78**	($1.22)	($3.22)
7%	$7.15	$5.15	**$3.15**	$1.15	($0.85)
9%	**$9.52**	**$7.52**	**$5.52**	**$3.52**	**$1.52**
11%	$11.89	$9.89	**$7.89**	$5.89	$3.89
13%	$14.25	$12.25	**$10.25**	$8.25	$6.25

Table 4.12. (Continued)

Rotation with Clearfield® Canola	Low-Disturbance Tillage				
	Tech Fee ($/Acre)				
	$3	$5	$7	$9	$11
Increase in Yield					
3%	$11.84	$9.84	**$7.84**	$5.84	$3.84
5%	$14.21	$12.21	**$10.21**	$8.21	$6.21
7%	$16.58	$14.58	**$12.58**	$10.58	$8.58
9%	**$18.95**	**$16.95**	**$14.95**	**$12.95**	**$10.95**
11%	$21.32	$19.32	**$17.32**	$15.32	$13.32
13%	$23.68	$21.68	**$19.68**	$17.68	$15.68

Rotation with Clearfield® Canola	Conventional Tillage				
	Tech Fee ($/Acre)				
	$3	$5	$7	$9	$11
Increase in Yield					
3%	$10.06	$8.06	**$6.06**	$4.06	$2.06
5%	$12.43	$10.43	**$8.43**	$6.43	$4.43
7%	$14.80	$12.80	**$10.80**	$8.80	$6.80
9%	**$17.17**	**$15.17**	**$13.17**	**$11.17**	**$9.17**
11%	$19.53	$17.53	**$15.53**	$13.53	$11.53
13%	$21.90	$19.90	**$17.90**	$15.90	$13.90

Rotation with Liberty Link® Canola	Low-Disturbance Tillage				
	Tech Fee ($/Acre)				
	$3	$5	$7	$9	$11
Increase in Yield					
3%	$11.84	$9.84	**$7.84**	$5.84	$3.84
5%	$14.21	$12.21	**$10.21**	$8.21	$6.21
7%	$16.58	$14.58	**$12.58**	$10.58	$8.58
9%	**$18.95**	**$16.95**	**$14.95**	**$12.95**	**$10.95**
11%	$21.32	$19.32	**$17.32**	$15.32	$13.32
13%	$23.68	$21.68	**$19.68**	$17.68	$15.68

Table 4.12. (Continued)

Rotation with Liberty Link® Canola			Conventional Tillage		
			Tech Fee ($/Acre)		
	$3	$5	$7	$9	$11
Increase in Yield					
3%	$10.06	$8.06	**$6.06**	$4.06	$2.06
5%	$12.43	$10.43	**$8.43**	$6.43	$4.43
7%	$14.80	$12.80	**$10.80**	$8.80	$6.80
9%	**$17.17**	**$15.17**	**$13.17**	**$11.17**	**$9.17**
11%	$19.53	$17.53	**$15.53**	$13.53	$11.53
13%	$21.90	$19.90	**$17.90**	$15.90	$13.90

In rotation with Roundup Ready® canola using conventional tillage we estimate negative farm-level benefits from adopting Roundup Ready® wheat when we use low yield and high technology fee assumptions (this is also true under one of the low-disturbance tillage scenarios). For those values of the yield increase and technology fee that we consider most plausible, however, the results show a positive benefit to adopting Roundup Ready® wheat, even when growing Roundup Ready®canola the following year. The estimated benefits are larger with conventional, Clearfield®, or Liberty Link® canola, compared to Roundup Ready® canola. To avoid undue complexity, we assume that the canola crop is fixed in each rotation, and the only change is from conventional to Roundup Ready® wheat. If the type of canola crop were allowed to change as well, this increased flexibility would translate into higher farm-level benefits than shown in Table 4.12.

Table 4.13 shows the estimated farm-level benefits in the dark brown soil zone. The first two panels show the single-year benefits of Roundup Ready® wheat over conventional wheat, for both low-disturbance and conventional tillage. The estimated benefits range from $7.80 to $19.00 per acre, using our baseline yield assumptions and allowing the technology fee to vary. The results of combining Roundup Ready® wheat with a four-year rotation are given in the lower two panels. In this case, the rotation is wheat-flax-canary seed-lentils. For the technology fees and the yield increases that we consider most likely, the benefits to the producer are positive in all cases, and we expect farm-level benefits to range from $11.80 to $17.96 per acre.

Table 4.13: Farm-Level Benefits of Adopting Roundup Ready® Wheat in the Dark Brown Soil Zone

| Single-Year | | | | Low-Disturbance Tillage | |
| | | | Tech Fee ($/Acre) | | |
	$3	$5	$7	$9	$11
Increase in Yield					
3%	$11.89	$9.89	$7.89	$5.89	$3.89
5%	$14.26	$12.26	$10.26	$8.26	$6.26
7%	$16.63	$14.63	$12.63	$10.63	$8.63
9%	$19.00	$17.00	$15.00	$13.00	$11.00
11%	$21.36	$19.36	$17.36	$15.36	$13.36
13%	$23.73	$21.73	$19.73	$17.73	$15.73

| Single-Year | | | | Conventional Tillage | |
| | | | Tech Fee ($/Acre) | | |
	$3	$5	$7	$9	$11
Increase in Yield					
3%	$8.69	$6.69	$4.69	$2.69	$0.69
5%	$11.06	$9.06	$7.06	$5.06	$3.06
7%	$13.43	$11.43	$9.43	$7.43	$5.43
9%	$15.80	$13.80	$11.80	$9.80	$7.80
11%	$18.16	$16.16	$14.16	$12.16	$10.16
13%	$20.53	$18.53	$16.53	$14.53	$12.53

| Rotation with Flax, Canary Seed, Lentils | | | | Low-Disturbance Tillage | |
| | | | Tech Fee ($/Acre) | | |
	$3	$5	$7	$9	$11
Increase in Yield					
3%	$14.85	$12.85	$10.85	$8.85	$6.85
5%	$17.22	$15.22	$13.22	$11.22	$9.22
7%	$19.59	$17.59	$15.59	$13.59	$11.59
9%	$21.96	$19.96	$17.96	$15.96	$13.96
11%	$24.33	$22.33	$20.33	$18.33	$16.33
13%	$26.69	$24.69	$22.69	$20.69	$18.69

Table 4.13. (Continued)

Rotation with Flax, Canary Seed, Lentils			Conventional Tillage		
			Tech Fee ($/Acre)		
	$3	$5	$7	$9	$11
Increase in Yield					
3%	$8.69	$6.69	$4.69	$2.69	$0.69
5%	$11.06	$9.06	$7.06	$5.06	$3.06
7%	$13.43	$11.43	$9.43	$7.43	$5.43
9%	$15.80	$13.80	$11.80	$9.80	$7.80
11%	$18.16	$16.16	$14.16	$12.16	$10.16
13%	$20.53	$18.53	$16.53	$14.53	$12.53

One interesting result is that benefits from adopting Roundup Ready® wheat are higher in the low-disturbance tillage rotation than the single year benefits (ignoring rotational considerations). Typically, we would expect the benefits within a rotation to be smaller, due to the need to control volunteer herbicide resistant wheat. In this case, however, the herbicides applied to the following flax crop perform this function without the addition of Assure to control volunteer Roundup Ready® wheat.

Finally, Table 4.14 presents the estimated farm-level benefits for the brown soil zone. The first two panels show the results for single-year benefits from adopting Roundup Ready® wheat. The estimated benefits are positive, with the exception of the lowest yield increase and the highest technology fee case. The expected benefits range from $9.60 to $12.80 per acre. The last two panels show the benefits to adoption as part of a four-year rotation. The conventional wheat rotation is wheat-fallow-durum-fallow, and the rotation with Roundup Ready® wheat is Roundup Ready® wheat-fallow-durum-fallow. Estimates of the farm-level benefits are mostly positive over the range of yield increase and technology fees that we analyze; the expected benefit is from $8.67 to $9.60 per acre. We estimate benefits to be negative with conventional tillage only with the outlier assumptions of $11/acre technology fee, and a low yield increase of 3%. With low disturbance tillage; benefits are negative for technology fees of $9-11 with the lowest yield scenario, and also with a 5% increase in yield and an $11 technology fee.

GENETICALLY MODIFIED WHEAT

Table 4.14: Farm-Level Benefits of Adopting Roundup Ready® Wheat in the Brown Soil Zone

Single-Year				Low-Disturbance Tillage	
			Tech Fee ($/Acre)		
	$3	$5	$7	$9	$11
Increase in Yield					
3%	$9.69	$7.69	$5.69	$3.69	$1.69
5%	$12.06	$10.06	$8.06	$6.06	$4.06
7%	$14.43	$12.43	$10.43	$8.43	$6.43
9%	$16.80	$14.80	$12.80	$10.80	$8.80
11%	$19.16	$17.16	$15.16	$13.16	$11.16
13%	$21.53	$19.53	$17.53	$15.53	$13.53

Single-Year				Conventional Tillage	
			Tech Fee ($/Acre)		
	$3	$5	$7	$9	$11
Increase in Yield					
3%	$6.49	$4.49	$2.49	$0.49	($1.51)
5%	$8.86	$6.86	$4.86	$2.86	$0.86
7%	$11.23	$9.23	$7.23	$5.23	$3.23
9%	$13.60	$11.60	$9.60	$7.60	$5.60
11%	$15.96	$13.96	$11.96	$9.96	$7.96
13%	$18.33	$16.33	$14.33	$12.33	$10.33

Rotation				Low-Disturbance Tillage	
			Tech Fee ($/Acre)		
	$3	$5	$7	$9	$11
Increase in Yield					
3%	$5.56	$3.56	$1.56	($0.44)	($2.44)
5%	$7.93	$5.93	$3.93	$1.93	($0.07)
7%	$10.30	$8.30	$6.30	$4.30	$2.30
9%	$12.67	$10.67	$8.67	$6.67	$4.67
11%	$15.04	$13.04	$11.04	$9.04	$7.04
13%	$17.40	$15.40	$13.40	$11.40	$9.40

Table 4.14. (Continued)

Rotation				Conventional Tillage	
			Tech Fee ($/Acre)		
	$3	$5	$7	$9	$11
Increase in Yield					
3%	$6.49	$4.49	**$2.49**	$0.49	($1.51)
5%	$8.86	$6.86	**$4.86**	$2.86	$0.86
7%	$11.23	$9.23	**$7.23**	$5.23	$3.23
9%	$13.60	$11.60	**$9.60**	$7.60	$5.60
11%	$15.96	$13.96	**$11.96**	$9.96	$7.96
13%	$18.33	$16.33	**$14.33**	$12.33	$10.33

To summarize, the farm-level results presented here and in Holzman and Furtan, Gray, and Holzman (2003b) indicate that the adoption of Roundup Ready® wheat can lead to a very large increase in profitability at the farm level. When considering the desirability of commercial production of Roundup Ready® wheat, however, the policy decision is more complicated. Merely finding the expected farm-level benefits to be positive ignores the underlying uncertainty inherent with new technology that is irreversible.

The approach recommended by the Industry Working Group on Roundup Ready® wheat for analyzing the decision under uncertainty is that suggested by Furtan, Gray, and Holzman (2003b): the *real options* approach. This is a more conservative decision rule than the standard net present value criterion often used. Even with the more conservative criteria, our results reported below indicate that the real options test is passed, and that the optimal decision for the Canadian government is to license Roundup Ready® wheat. We provide a detailed explanation of the real options approach to decision-making and our results for Roundup Ready® wheat in a later section.

Stochastic Simulations. The previous results represent the expected economic benefits from adoption of Roundup Ready® wheat for different levels of projected yield increases. To gain further understanding of the impact of Roundup Ready® wheat at the farm level, we specify probability distributions for important cost and return variables, and perform Monte Carlo simulation analysis. The variables for which we specify probability distributions are the Roundup Ready® wheat yield (Y_{GM}), unit price of Roundup Ready® wheat (P_{GM}), and the price premium of conventional wheat over GM wheat ($P_C - P_{GM}$). We take 10,000 draws from these distributions in order to estimate a confidence interval for the bottom-line change in per acre net returns from adoption.

We assume that the price of wheat is normally distributed, with a mean of $4.00 per bushel, and a standard deviation of $0.40 per bushel. The price premium for conventional wheat is modeled with a triangular distribution. The minimum value of the price premium is $0.05, the maximum value is $0.25 per bushel, and the most likely value is $0.15 per bushel. The yield for Roundup Ready® wheat is also assumed to be triangular.[86] The minimum average yield for Roundup Ready® wheat is 29.7 bushels per acre (a 0.34% increase in yield over conventional wheat). The maximum yield for Roundup Ready® wheat is 34.7 bushels per acre (a 17.4% increase), and the most likely value is 32.3 bushels per acre (about 9% higher than conventional wheat).

The Monte Carlo results for the black soil zone are reported in Table 4.15. The advantage of the Monte Carlo simulation is that we can generate confidence intervals for the net benefits. In Table 4.15 we report the mean value, as well as a 90% confidence interval for the benefits of adoption. The column labeled "5%" gives the lower bound of the confidence interval, and the column labeled "95%" gives the upper bound. This table shows the benefits from adopting Roundup Ready® wheat both in isolation, and as part of a rotation with both conventional canola and Roundup Ready® canola.

Table 4.15: Black Soil Zone Monte Carlo Results, per Acre Benefits

	5%	Mean	95%
RR Wheat, Single Year			
Low-Disturbance Tillage	$11.22	$18.44	$25.94
Conventional Tillage	$5.78	$13.00	$20.50
RR Wheat Rotation with Conventional Canola			
Low-Disturbance Tillage	$7.56	$14.78	$22.29
Conventional Tillage	$5.78	$13.00	$20.50
RR Wheat Rotation with RR Canola			
Low-Disturbance Tillage	$3.57	$10.79	$18.30
Conventional Tillage	$(1.87)	$5.35	$12.86
RR Wheat Rotation with Clearfield® Canola			
Low-Disturbance Tillage	$7.56	$14.78	$22.29
Conventional Tillage	$5.78	$13.00	$20.50
RR Wheat Rotation with Liberty Link® Canola			
Low-Disturbance Tillage	$7.56	$14.78	$22.29
Conventional Tillage	$5.78	$13.00	$20.50

For a single-year, the mean value for the estimated net benefit of adoption is $13.00 per acre with conventional tillage practices, and the confidence interval is from $5.78 to $20.50 per acre. The benefits are higher with low-disturbance tillage: the confidence interval is from $11.22 to $25.94, with a mean value of $18.44 per acre. In rotation with conventional canola, Clearfield® canola or Liberty Link® canola, the confidence interval is $7.56 to $22.29 per acre for low-disturbance tillage, and from $5.78 to $20.50 per acre for conventional tillage. The estimated net benefits to Roundup Ready® wheat adoption are lower in rotation with Roundup Ready® canola. The confidence interval is from $3.57 to $18.30 per acre for low-disturbance tillage, and -$1.87 to $12.86 per acre for conventional tillage. Even in this worst case scenario, however, the estimated net benefits to adoption are positive more than 87% of the time.

The Monte Carlo results for the dark brown soil zone are reported in Table 4.16. For a single year, the 90% confidence interval is from $7.75 to $22.14 per acre for low-disturbance tillage, and $4.55 to $18.94 per acre for conventional tillage. Within a four year rotation, the confidence interval is $4.55 to $18.94 per acre for conventional tillage, and $10.72 to $25.11 per acre for low-disturbance tillage, which is the tillage pattern with the smallest estimated benefits in this soil zone. The estimates of net benefits were positive in all cases.

Table 4.16: Dark Brown Zone Monte Carlo Results, per Acre Benefits

	5%	Mean	95%
RR Wheat, One Year, Low-Disturbance	$7.75	$14.86	$22.14
RR Wheat, One Year, Conventional	$4.55	$11.66	$18.94
RR Wheat, Rotation, Low-Disturbance	$10.72	$17.83	$25.11
RR Wheat, Rotation, Conventional	$4.55	$11.66	$18.94

The Monte Carlo results for the brown soil zone are reported in Table 4.17. The structure of the table is the same as above. For a single year, the 90% confidence interval for the benefits of Roundup Ready® wheat is from $5.42 to $20.30 per acre for low-disturbance tillage, and lower for conventional tillage: $2.22 to $17.10 per acre. As part of a rotation, the confidence interval is from $1.29 to $16.18 per acre for low-disturbance tillage, and $2.22 to $17.10 per acre for conventional tillage. The estimated benefits are lowest when using low-disturbance tillage within a rotation. Even in that case, however, the benefits are positive more than 97% of the time.

Table 4.17: Brown Zone Monte Carlo Results, per Acre Benefits

	5%	Mean	95%
RR Wheat, One Year, Low-Disturbance	$5.42	$12.75	$20.30
RR Wheat, One Year, Conventional	$2.22	$9.55	$17.10
RR Wheat, Rotation, Low-Disturbance	$1.29	$8.63	$16.18
RR Wheat, Rotation, Conventional	$2.22	$9.55	$17.10

Aggregate Benefits and Costs of Genetically Modified Wheat under Uncertainty: Real Options Results

Background

This section focuses on the aggregate industry-wide benefits and costs of introducing Roundup Ready® wheat in western Canada. The policy issues involved in this decision were discussed in the introductory chapter; the material here presents the assumptions we use and the estimates we find for the industry benefits and costs of Roundup Ready® wheat. This section explains one approach that we use to study the question of introduction, that of "real options." The real options approach is particularly well-suited to irreversible dynamic questions that feature significant uncertainty, such as the introduction of Roundup Ready® wheat. Because it accounts for uncertainty and irreversibility, the real options approach is more conservative than the traditional benefit-cost or net present value analysis.

Similar work has been published by Furtan, Gray, and Holzman (2003b). They were the first to suggest the real options approach as the correct decision rule for the adoption of GM wheat. Their results suggest that the benefit-cost ratio is not yet sufficiently high to indicate that introduction of Roundup Ready® wheat is the correct decision. The results of our research, however, are that the benefits to adoption of Roundup Ready® or other types of GM wheat are so great that introducing this technology into Canada is the correct decision.

This section begins with a brief review of the sources of the costs and benefits from adopting GM wheat at the farm and aggregate level. We report our assumptions and compare them with the assumptions made by Furtan, Gray, and Holzman (2003b) to facilitate comparison. First, we review the important elements of the decision to introduce Roundup Ready® or other GM wheat into Canada, including an explanation of using "real options" to analyze that decision. Then we present the results of our analysis, which indicates that introduction of GM wheat is a good economic decision, and we complete this section with an analysis of the sensitivity of our results to the assumptions we make.

Agronomic Impacts of GM wheat

At the most basic level, GM wheat is beneficial to the grower because it can increase yields and decrease costs. The best available work to date on the farm-level economics of GM wheat is Holzman. Our estimates of the farm-level benefits and costs are extensions of his model, as described above.

Sources of Benefits. GM crops that have already been commercialized have shown yield increases. Current agronomic research suggests that adoption of GM wheat will lead to an increase in yields (Blackshaw and Harker, and Kidnie et al. both report Canadian field trial results that show mean yield gains of a least 9%). Glyphosate tolerant wheat would allow the use of a non-selective herbicide during the growing season, decreasing weed infestation, and thereby increasing yields. Consistent with the published agronomic studies, our baseline assumption is that wheat yields will increase 9%. This is higher than Holzman who assumed a 6% baseline increase in yield. Furtan, Gray and Holzman (2003b) assumed a yield increase of only 3% in their work.

The yield increase is an estimate, because GM wheat has not been grown commercially. The yield gains we assume are similar to yield gains estimated for other genetically modified crops such as Bt corn (Marra, Pardey, and Alston; Koziel et al.) and canola (Canola Council of Canada). In addition to increased yields, GM wheat can also provide savings in herbicide costs.

Reductions in Cost Savings. There are additional cost considerations that must be included when estimating the net farm level benefits of adopting GM wheat. First, the owner of the GM technology must be compensated. This could occur through higher seed costs, bundled purchases of herbicide and seed, or what has been called a "technology use agreement" (TUA) or a "technology fee." Incorporating these additional costs through a technology fee is the simplest and most transparent, and it is the approach we take here. We assume that the technology fee will be set at $7 per acre. This estimate is lower than Holzman's estimate of $15, and on the low end of the $4 to $10 estimate by Furtan, Gray, and Holzman (2003b).

Second, there may be additional costs that occur within a crop rotation. Because wheat is grown in rotation with other crops, any impact on the cost of production of those other crops must also be considered. Volunteer GM wheat will require additional herbicides in a no-till system, and can reduce the benefits of GM canola if planted after the glyphosate resistant wheat. This phenomenon could also affect non-adopters if GM wheat is poorly handled, or if other plants become tolerant to glyphosate.

When analyzing Roundup Ready® wheat in a rotation, Holzman estimates the benefit of Roundup Ready® wheat at $5.13 per acre[87] when grown in a rotation with conventional canola using zero-tillage. There is no change from his single-year benefit estimate of $8.78 per acre with conventional tillage and a rotation including conventional canola. When Roundup Ready® canola is planted instead of conventional canola, Holzman's estimate of the benefits of Roundup Ready® wheat falls to 38 cents per acre with no-till and $4.96 per acre[88] with conventional tillage. For comparison, our results, including these additional costs are reported Tables 4.10 and 4.11, above.

Additional Costs beyond the Farm
The benefits of adopting GM wheat at the farm level are clear. When considering the introduction of GM wheat nationwide, there are other considerations, such as the impact of the introduction on the ability of the Canadian Wheat Board (CWB) to market the crop. The CWB has claimed that 82% of their current market will not accept GM wheat if introduced. We believe that is a large overestimate, as we discuss in Chapter 2. There are surely some buyers who will insist on conventional wheat, and they will have to pay a premium for it, as they do now with non-GM soybeans and corn. How that premium affects farm income is determined by how GM and conventional wheat is handled and marketed after harvest. Some in the industry have suggested that the non-GM wheat cannot be handled separately, so that both adopters (who enjoy the benefits of higher yield and lower costs) and non-adopters (who do not) will be forced to forego the price premium for conventional wheat. Chapter 3 considers the issues and costs involved in segregating wheat. For the purpose of our analysis here, we assume that GM and conventional wheat can be kept segregated until received by the buyer. There is a working model for this type of segregation in the corn and soybean market today. Segregation and identity preservation costs for non-GM wheat are estimated at $.15 per bushel in the Canadian system, which is higher than estimated in Chapter 3.[89] Finally, another potential cost is due to the impact of Roundup Ready wheat on the world market. Additional wheat production could cause the world wheat price to fall, if production increases and cost savings were large enough. We do not model that effect in this sec-

tion, assuming that Canada is a small country in the large wheat market that will accept genetically modified wheat, the same assumption used by Furtan, Gray and Holzman (2003b). This is a reasonable assumption, especially when analyzing the decision for Canada to license GM wheat in isolation. The general equilibrium impact of genetically modified wheat being introduced in other countries is the subject of the final section of this chapter.

Decision Criteria

Real options is a more modern technique than the standard benefit-cost or net present value methods that are often used to evaluate decisions of this kind. It explicitly accounts for uncertainty and irreversibility, both of which are important aspects of GM wheat introduction. We will briefly describe the real options approach, and how it can be used for decision-making. Then we will use the real options technique to evaluate the licensing of GM wheat in Canada, and discuss the sensitivity of our results to the assumptions used in the model.

The Real Options Approach

The use of real options as a decision-making tool began in the mid-1980s, with the work of McDonald and Siegel. They adapted theory developed for the pricing of financial options and applied it to making actual (real) business decisions. Since that time, the use of real options has become very popular, and the approach is well-suited for many public policy decisions.

Comparison to Traditional Cost/Benefit Analysis. The more traditional benefit-cost approach to evaluate decisions has been to calculate the present value of costs and benefits that occur in the future. According to this rule, if the present value of benefits exceeds the present value of costs, then the benefit-cost ratio is greater than one, and the project or policy should be undertaken. A benefit-cost ratio greater than one is equivalent to a positive net present value. There are certain drawbacks to this approach. First, it ignores the uncertainty inherent in estimating future costs and benefits. Second, it does not consider that some decisions are either expensive or impossible to reverse, and third it does not recognize the possibility of waiting for more information to arrive before making a decision.

Real options on the other hand, accounts for these factors. It's correct to think of real options as a more conservative decision rule than the standard benefit-cost decision. With real options, the benefit-cost ratio must be above some threshold level (often called a hurdle rate) before the decision to go ahead is made. The size of the hurdle depends on the nature of the uncertainty. If there was no uncertainty, then the real options threshold level would be equivalent to the standard benefit-cost criterion, where the benefit-cost ratio must be greater than one. With more uncertainty, the threshold is higher. The intuition behind the higher threshold is that the actual benefits and costs will be different than forecast. If the benefit-cost ratio is below the critical threshold, it's best to wait and acquire more information before deciding to adopt a policy. Above the threshold, the potential benefits are so high that the value of more information is lower than the cost of delay. For example, delaying the introduction of GM wheat in Canada for ten years would certainly allow the accumulation of more information about the agronomic and environmental characteristics and market acceptance, but at the very real cost of foregone benefits to prairie wheat farmers. The level of the threshold is determined by the type of uncertainty. More uncertainty yields a higher threshold, and a larger upward trend in the benefit-cost ratio over time yields a lower threshold.

Furtan, Gray, and Holzman (2003b) perform the calculations suggested by McDonald and Siegel and calculate a real options threshold ratio of 2.27.[90] To summarize, that result means that the benefits of introduction must be at least 2.27 times the cost of introduction before commercialization of GM wheat is a good decision for western Canada. We use the threshold calculated by Furtan, Gray, and Holzman (2003b) as well, to make our results comparable to theirs. Although we use the same decision rule, using out assumptions we find that the benefit-cost ratio is well over 2.27.

The real options model originates with the work of McDonald and Siegel. This is not to be confused with the Black-Scholes option pricing model. McDonald and Siegel specifically designed their model to value real options rather than financial options, whereas the Black-Scholes model was developed specifically for financial options. The option value obtained from Mcdonald and Siegel can be derived independently from Black-Scholes, but there are similarities. For instance, the nature of the uncertainty in this model (the Brownian motion) is the same as that used by Black and Scholes. Also, the conditions that McDonald and Siegel use to solve the partial differential equation (smooth pasting and value matching) are the same as in the Black-Scholes equation.

The assumptions of the real options model are not without controversy, especially that of the dynamics of the economic variables (i.e., the Brownian motion assumption). However, we agree with the Industry Working Group on GM Wheat that there is an option value associated with this technology, and ignoring it would be a mistake, even if it is hard to estimate.

If lack of confidence with the assumptions of the real options model is high enough to lead to its rejection, the obvious question is "what decision making criterion should be used instead of the option value approach?" Net Present Value, ignoring the uncertainty in the world, is too simplistic. If the goal is to estimate the benefit-cost hurdle rate in any scientific way, you are going to end up with an option value model. Furtan, Gray and Holzman conduct sensitivity analysis for the parameters in their real option model, which gives an indication of whether or not the hurdle rate is robust.

Uncertainty. There are some technical considerations associated with the real options approach that we discuss briefly, without presenting the detailed theoretical underpinnings. At the basic level, the decision maker is assumed to be learning whether benefits and costs are likely to be higher or lower in the future. If waiting does not yield this additional information, then there is no point in waiting to make a decision. Specifically, decision makers must assume that the benefits and costs will start at today's observed value, and then move randomly in the future. It is reasonable to expect that this may have a tendency to trend upwards or downwards, in addition to displaying some random unpredictable movement.

Irreversibility. If a policy decision is easily reversed, then the value of waiting for more information is diminished. If a decision is reversible, then the decision maker should adopt a policy with a benefit-cost ratio greater than one, and reverse it if the forecast turns out to be incorrect. Irreversibility does not necessarily mean that it is impossible to reverse a policy choice; rather it means that it will be expensive to do so.

Option Value. The term "option" in a real option framework is an important one, because it describes a specific choice that can be made. The choice is not whether to "license GM wheat" or "not license," but instead "license GM wheat today" or "wait, and decide tomorrow." By delaying the decision, the decision maker is keeping the option of adopting alive. Keeping the option alive has value, a value that the real options theory allows us to quantify. Recognizing that the option itself has value is at the heart of the real options framework. The option value is the value of waiting, and it stems from the benefit of taking additional time to learn and the consequent reduction of the decision maker's uncertainty.

It is important to understand the relationship between the option value and the real option threshold (or hurdle rate) discussed above. Reaching the threshold is equivalent to the option value of waiting falling to zero. As long as the benefit-cost ratio is below the hurdle, the option value is positive, and the option to license GM wheat should be not exercised. Instead, the decision maker should continue to wait. If the benefit-cost ratio is equal to or above the threshold, the option value is zero. There is no need for additional information to make a wise decision, and delaying the benefits of adoption is a mistake. For our needs, because the option value concept and the threshold level are equivalent, we will be presenting our results in terms of the benefit-cost ratio, rather than option value.

An important aspect of the real option approach is to re-evaluate the benefits and costs, so that we can observe when the threshold is reached. If GM wheat is not licensed now, should it be licensed in the future? If so, when is that likely to be? If the benefit-cost ratio is close to the threshold, or if it might trend upward due to technological innovation, then a decision to not license GM wheat should be re-evaluated periodically. By using the real options approach, policy-makers are recognizing that this is not a one-time decision, but really a policy of licensing GM wheat as soon as the threshold is met.

Assumptions Used in Real Options Analysis
The baseline assumptions used in our analysis are given in Tables 4.4 – 4.8. We expect, based on the history of other GM crops discussed in Chapter 1 that about 75% of total wheat acreage in the Canadian prairie will be planted to GM wheat. GM wheat yields are expected to be 9% higher than conventional yields, but herbicide costs are expected to be lower than conventional wheat. The herbicide cost reduction will vary by farm and by soil zone, but we estimate that cost savings will be just over $12 per acre across the prairies, on average. This figure was found by calculating the herbicide savings for each rotation, soil zone, and tillage practice, and then finding an average savings, weighted by the share of acreage in each soil zone.

Furtan, Gray and Holzman (2003b) also estimate what they call the "environmental cost" of introducing GM wheat. For adopters, this cost represents the reduced benefits of planting GM wheat when the cost of controlling volunteer herbicide-resistant wheat is considered. Furtan, Gray and Holzman (2003b) assumed a cost for volunteer GM wheat control of about $2 per acre for adopters. Our estimate of the cost of volunteer control for adopters is based on our research on the farm-level benefits. As described earlier in this chapter, we estimated the benefits to adoption of GM wheat both in a single year and within a four year rotation. The difference between the single-year benefits and the benefits in a rotation is our estimate of volunteer control costs for adopters of GM wheat. To find an aggregate cost of volunteer control for adopters, we used a weighted average, with the weights being the share of total prairie wheat acreage in each soil zone, and within the black soil zone the share of acreage planted to each of the four canola types (conventional, Roundup Ready®, Clearfield® and Liberty Link®) we analyze. Because the costs of volunteer GM wheat control vary by tillage practice, we assumed that 70% of the total acreage uses low-disturbance tillage, and 30% uses conventional tillage. Our estimate for the cost of volunteer control is just under $2.00 per acre. There may be unforeseen costs, however, and in our analysis at the aggregate level, we use a more conservative $4.00 per acre. Furtan, Gray and Holzman (2003b) also assume that non-adopters have an environmental cost about half the size of the cost to adopters. For consistency, we maintain that ratio and set the non-adopter cost of volunteer control at $2.00 per acre.

Results of the Real Options model

Given the assumptions in Table 4.18, the annual expected benefits and costs are set forth in Table 4.19. The estimated annual net benefits of GM wheat introduction are over $320 million for the Canadian prairies. In addition to providing total benefits and costs, and net benefits, Table 4.19 also reports estimated benefits by sector. The estimated benefits to growers who adopt the technology are about $287 million per year. The returns to the provider of the GM wheat through payment of technology fees are listed as "Technology Supplier Benefits," and they are estimated at $105 million per year. Benefits to non-adopters of GM wheat due to a price premium for conventional wheat are estimated at about $22 million per year. Additional costs of GM wheat are also listed in the table. These are rotation and volunteer control costs estimated to be $60 million per year for adopters of GM wheat, rotation and volunteer control costs for non-adopters of GM wheat estimated to be $10 million per year, and sector-wide segregation costs estimated to be about $22 million per year.

Table 4.18. Baseline Assumptions for Real Options Calculations

Total Acreage	20,000,000 acres
GM Wheat Adopters	75%
Non-Adopters	25%
GM Wheat Adopters	15,000,000 acres
Non-Adopters	5,000,000 acres
GM Wheat Price	$4.00/bu
Non-GM Price	$4.15/bu
Non-GM Price Premium	$0.15/bu
GM Wheat Yield	32.3 bu/acre
Non-GM Yield	29.6 bu/acre
GM Wheat Seed Cost	$12.38/acre
Non-GM Seed Cost	$12.38/acre
GM Wheat Technology fee	$7.00/acre
GM Wheat Volunteer Control Cost	$4/acre
Non-GM Volunteer Control Cost	$2/acre
Segregation Cost	$0.15/bu
Discount Rate	8%

Table 4.19. Annual Benefits and Costs of Roundup Ready® Wheat (thousands of dollars)

Net Benefits	$322,833
Total Benefits	$415,033
Total Costs	$92,200
Adopter Benefits	$287,833
Technology Supplier Benefits	$105,000
Non-Adopter Market Benefits	$22,200
Adopter Rotation and Volunteer Control Cost	$60,000
Non-Adopter Rotation and Volunteer Control Cost	$10,000
Segregation Cost	$22,200

Table 4.20. Present Value of Benefits and Costs (thousands of dollars)

Net Benefits	$4,035,409
Total Benefits	$5,187,909
Total Costs	$1,152,500
Adopter Returns	$3,597,909
Benefit-Cost Ratio	4.50
Benefit-Cost Ratio (Producers only)	3.36

The estimated benefits are high enough relative to the estimated costs that the benefit-cost ratio is well above the real option threshold. Table 4.20 shows the present value of the costs and benefits of introducing GM wheat, as well as the benefit-cost ratio, which is 4.50. The estimated benefit-cost ratio is 3.36 for producers only, a measure suggested by Furtan, Gray and Holzman (2003b). We believe this measure gives a misleading interpretation, because it ignores the benefits to the owner of the technology. It is presented here only for comparison purposes with the results of Furtan, Gray and Holzman (2003b).

In both cases, the benefit-cost ratio is well above the threshold level of 2.27 to recommend adoption of GM wheat in western Canada.

Comparison to Furtan, Gray, and Holzman
Furtan, Gray, and Holzman (2003b) also used real options analysis to evaluate whether this is a good time to commercialize Roundup Ready® wheat in western Canada. In fact, we use their estimate of the real options benefit-cost threshold as our decision rule. Although our methods are similar, our results are different; we find that immediate commercialization is the correct decision, and we conclude that their results are somewhat ambiguous. Many of the differences between our model and theirs are simply differences in the numeric value of certain assumptions, and others are a result of more fundamental differences in approach.

Among the more fundamental differences is our treatment of the price gap between GM wheat and non-GM wheat. Furtan, Gray, and Holzman (2003b) view the difference in price as a discount from the world price of wheat that adopters of GM wheat will suffer, and they estimate this discount to be $0.20 per bushel. Based on existing GM and non-GM markets, such as corn and soybeans, we feel that GM wheat will receive the world price for wheat. Non-GM wheat will become a specialty product that will receive a price premium, just as non-GM corn and soybeans do. For those reasons, we view the difference in price as a benefit to non-adopters who can sell into the higher value market, and we estimate that premium at $0.15 per bushel.

Another important difference between our work and Furtan et. al. is in the treatment of segregation costs. We assume that non-GM wheat will be segregated from GM wheat, and that it will be identity preserved so that it can be sold into the higher valued market. Furtan, Gray, and Holzman (2003b), have two different assumptions about segregation.

First, they assume segregation at zero cost. In that case, there is no price discount to non-adopters, and they find a benefit-cost ratio of 2.80, well above their published real options threshold of 2.27 for adopting GM wheat. Their other model assumes that it is not possible to segregate GM wheat from non-GM wheat. In this case, all Canadian wheat faces a discount from the prevailing world price, and Furtan, Gray, and Holzman (2003b) estimate the cost-benefit ratio of 2.18, just under their real options threshold. We feel that both of these assumptions regarding segregation are incorrect. Experience with other crops suggests that non-GM wheat can be successfully segregated, but this segregation will not be costless; the zero segregation cost assumption of Furtan, Gray, and Holzman (2003b) is not realistic. Although they do not estimate a cost of segregation, their published work allows the calculation of a maximum value for segregation costs that forces the benefit/cost ratio to the real options threshold. Using all their assumptions for the model where GM and non-GM wheat is segregated, if the segregation costs are less than $0.50 per bushel, the benefit/cost ratio is above their real options threshold of 2.27. This is assuming that the segregation costs are applied to the smaller segment of the wheat market, the non-GM wheat, and that these costs reduce the net benefit of introducing GM wheat. Although our benefit/cost calculations use a conservative cost estimate for segregation of $0.15 per bushel, the implied estimate by Furtan, Gray, and Holzman (2003b) is a very high estimate of the true costs. See Chapter 3 for more discussion on the segregation of GM crops.

We treat the cost of segregation only as a cost, and do not include any benefits that may accrue to those providing segregation services beyond the farm gate, such as grain companies and handlers.

There are other differences in the values of parameters assumed by Furtan, Gray, and Holzman (2003b) and the values that we use. The first is the technology fee charged to growers of GM crops. We model the technology fee as $7 per acre, and Furtan, Gray, and Holzman (2003b) assume a technology fee of $4 per acre with costless segregation, and $10 per acre with no segregation of non-GM wheat. Our cost of volunteer control ($4 for adopters of GM wheat, and $2 for non-adopters of GM wheat) is higher than the cost assumed by Furtan, Gray, and Holzman (2003b) of $2 for adopters and $1 for non-adopters. Finally, our estimate of the increased yield to GM wheat (9%) is consistent with published field trials, and larger than Furtan, Gray, and Holzman's (2003b) estimate of a 3% yield increase.

Sensitivity of the Results

It is useful to change the assumptions in the real options model, in order to see how robust the results are. In this section, we show how the benefit-cost ratio changes as the underlying assumptions change, in all cases comparing them to the real options adoption threshold. The threshold itself is sensitive to assumptions (primarily the assumptions about the amount of uncertainty) as well, but we don't present that information here.

The following charts show how the benefit-cost ratio changes as the parameters change. In Figures 4.1 through 4.4, the dashed line is the real options benefit-cost hurdle of 2.27, and the solid line represents the benefit-cost ratio for different scenarios. Only one assumption changes at a time on the following charts; all of the others remain at their baseline levels reported in Table 4.18.

The first chart (Figure 4.1) shows the sensitivity of the benefit-cost ratio (in present value) to changes in the segregation costs. At low segregation costs, the benefit cost ratio for the industry is well above (roughly double) the real options threshold. The benefit-cost ratio remains above the threshold throughout the range of segregation costs, even when they increase to 40 cents per bushel. We do not count the segregation costs as a benefit to the grain handling industry, but merely as a cost that reduces net revenues to the prairie grain sector.

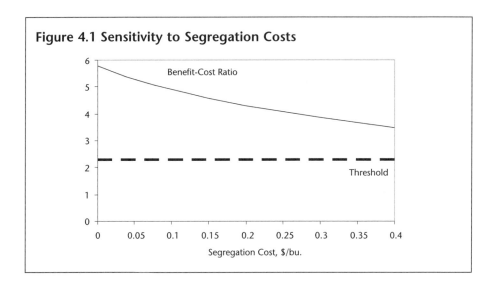

Figure 4.1 Sensitivity to Segregation Costs

Figure 4.2 shows the sensitivity of the benefit-cost estimate to an increasing price premium received by non-GM producers. Even at a relatively low premium, the benefit-cost ratio is over 4.0, because growers who adopt GM wheat capture the cost savings and yield benefits. As the premium increases, the benefit-cost ratio increases, because of the benefits that accrue to the non-adopters.

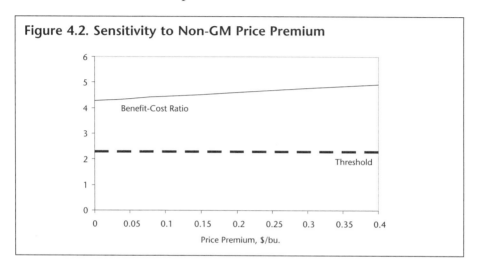

Figure 4.2. Sensitivity to Non-GM Price Premium

Figure 4.3 shows the effect of changing the yield advantage of GM wheat from 3% to 13%. The results are as expected, because higher yields lead to higher benefits of adoption. Even with a low yield advantage assumption, the benefit cost ratio is well above the threshold of 2.27.

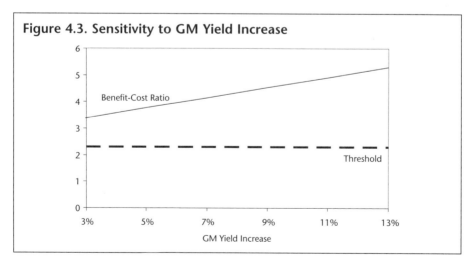

Figure 4.3. Sensitivity to GM Yield Increase

Figure 4.4 shows the sensitivity of the benefit-cost ratio to changes in the technology fee. Unlike the above charts, this one has three lines instead of two. Two of the lines have the same meaning as on the earlier charts: the dashed line is the option value threshold, and the solid line is the benefit-cost ratio. In this case, the benefit-cost ratio does not change as the technology fee increases because the fee is a direct transfer from adopters of GM wheat to the owners of the technology. The distribution of benefits changes, but the overall level stays the same. A third line has been added to the chart, the benefit-cost ratio for producers only, the measure suggested by Furtan, Gray and Holzman (2003b). This is the dashed, downward sloping line on the chart. The line slopes downward because the benefits to producers are lower when they have to pay a larger technology fee. For the range of estimates studied here (from $3 to $11 per acre), however, the producer-only benefit-cost ratio remains above the real options adoption threshold.

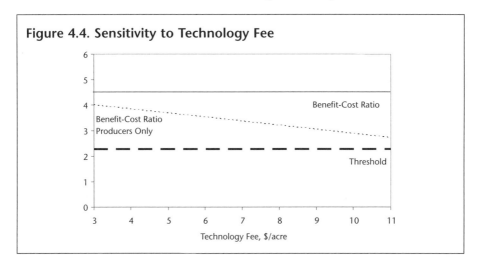

Figure 4.4. Sensitivity to Technology Fee

Global Aggregate Benefits and Costs of Genetically Modified Wheat
In order to further explore the economic effects of the commercialization of GM wheat, we now provide an estimate of the global economic welfare gains of adoption of this technology and the share of those gains that would be enjoyed by Canada. We estimate the changes from the baseline case of the wheat market today, when GM wheat is not produced commercially anywhere. To measure the cost of the policy decision to block commercialization of GM wheat in North America, we estimate the opportunity cost of foregoing GM wheat introduction. We compare the baseline case with our first adoption scenario, where GM wheat is adopted in Canada, the United States, and in developing countries.

Even though Canada has decided to not adopt GM wheat at this time, this does not mean that this technology will not be released elsewhere, such as in Argentina or in some other developing country. This possibility of third country release is the focus of our second adoption scenario, and we provide a point estimate of the loss to Canada assuming that release and adoption takes place outside of North America.

We use a numerical simulation model of the world wheat market developed by Gruère and Carter. In constructing the model, Gruère and Carter selected the world's largest traders and producers of wheat, and categorized them into three regions denoted as region A, region B and region C (see Table 4.21). Countries in region A are producers of GM crops and exporters of wheat, with a majority of tolerant consumers when it comes to the issue of GM foods. This region includes North America and Argentina.[91] Region B includes rich country wheat producers or importers preferring non-GM crops, with a large share of precautionary consumers. The EU, Japan and Korea are included in region B because of their support for mandatory GM labeling, and the anti-GM consumer attitudes in these parts of the world. Countries in region C are less developed countries, large producers and net importers of wheat, with consumers who are mostly tolerant regarding the question of GM foods. Summary wheat statistics for the three regions are presented in Table 4.21.

This model accounts for alternative national policies on GM food labeling and allows consumer acceptance of GM wheat to vary across the regions. The parameters are calibrated with aggregate data based on the 2001 FAO agricultural database. For each region, the quantity consumed is the sum of production and imports, minus exports. Summing individual country consumption yields the total consumption in 2001. Regions A and B have a constant total consumption of wheat before and after the introduction of GM wheat. In region C, with the introduction of GM wheat, total consumption of wheat is allowed to grow by up to 10% over the 2001 consumption level, because countries in region C have an extra capacity to absorb cheaper wheat (in economic terms, the demand is relatively price elastic in region C, and inelastic in the two other regions).

The model's cost coefficients are calibrated by using the average yearly world prices for wheat and the national production quantities in 2001. The non-GM wheat price is 2.5% above the 2001 reference world price, and the GM price of reference is 2.5% below this average price. The model assumes that the adoption of GM wheat increases yields by 10%.[92]

The total costs of segregation and testing are set equal to 5.3% of the reference average price. Carter and Gruère present results for three simulations, which differ by the degree of Roundup Ready® adoption among the three regions. Here we report one of their simulations where regions A and C each allocate 75% of production to GM wheat, and region B produces only non-GM wheat. Each region is subject to a capacity constraint: it cannot produce more than the aggregate production of wheat in 2001 unless it adopts GM wheat. Finally, the model assumes that tolerant consumers represent 85% of the consumers in region A, 10% in region B and 95% in region C. In order to account for the uncertainty surrounding these parameters, the model allows them to be randomly picked in each simulation. The specific parameters associated with this model are described in detail in Carter and Gruère (2004).

Table 4.21. Summary statistics underlying Gruère and Carter numerical model: 2001 (mmt) and percentage of the world level.

Country	Production	Imports	Exports
US	53.26	2.34	26.53
Canada	20.567	0.144	17.91
Argentina	15.3	0.003	11.3
Region A Total	89.128	2.49	55.75
Japan	0.7	5.52	0.44
Korea	0.003	3.63	0.036
EU	92.09	3.96	15.39
Region B Total	92.79	13.11	15.87
Algeria	2	4.56	0
Brazil	3.26	7.26	0.002
China	93.87	1.8	0.82
Egypt	6.25	4.44	0.02
India	68.76	0.004	3.09
Iran	9.46	6.44	0.017
Morocco	3.316	3.378	0.174
Russia	46.87	1.02	1.87
Region C Total	233.81	28.91	5.99
Total all regions	415.73 (70%)	44.51 (45%)	77.61 (72%)

Source: Gruère and Carter (2004), derived from FAO database (www.fao.org).

The threshold levels for adventitious presence of GM depend on the regulations for each scenario. Under current regulations these will be 5% for region A, 0.9% for region B, and 5% for region C. For each labeling policy and each scenario Carter and Gruère ran 10,000 simulations, each of them drawing the parameters according to their distributions.

Estimated producer surplus changes with the introduction of GM wheat are reported in Table 4.22. This is our first adoption scenario and it assumes release in Canada, the US, Argentina, and other key developing countries. Canada is part of Region A and the welfare impact on Canada is broken out of Region A for purposes of reporting the results in Table 4.22. Region A producers gain from the adoption of GM wheat. These results show an annual producer welfare gain of $134 million for Canada from adoption and a total of $582 million producer gain for region A including Canada. As region B produces only non-GM, producers in this region will gain with the current regulations, which would allow them to sell non-GM wheat at a high price with a cost advantage compared to the other regions (producers of non-GM wheat in B incur only testing costs and have no segregation costs). Producers in C would gain an estimated $1.6 billion per year due to lower production costs. This underscores the fact that developing countries will benefit greatly from the introduction of genetically modified wheat.

Region B consumers will be opposed to any introduction of GM wheat, because the price of conventional wheat will rise. Alternatively, Region C consumers will support the introduction of GM wheat because the price of GM wheat will be lower than the baseline price. The absolute benefits of GM for consumers in region C is larger than that obtained by consumers in A and B, because the consumption of wheat in region C is twice as large as the aggregate consumption in regions A and B.

What happens if North America (along with the EU and Japan and Korea) rejects GM wheat but the major developing countries go ahead with release and adoption? The estimated outcome of this second scenario is reported in Table 4.23. If the current set of labeling regulations remain in place, then Canada would lose an estimated $138 million per year, and Canadian wheat farmers would stand to lose about $100 million per year. If Canada makes this choice, which is has for now, there is little overall impact on the developing world or on the EU (compare the results in Table 4.22 and 4.23 for these regions).

Table 4.22. Estimated Change in Annual Economic Welfare with Introduction of GM Wheat Outside of the EU and Japan ($Million: 2001)

Absolute Changes in $million/yr	Canada	Region A	Region B	Region C	Sum
Producer Surplus	134	448	230	1,666	2,479
Consumer Surplus	6	80	-655	2,042	1,467
Total Surplus	141	522	-425	3,708	3,946

Source: Calculated from Gruère and Carter (2004) model.

[a] Current regulations are a mixture of voluntary and mandatory labeling across regions.

[b] Mandatory labeling regulations in every country.

[c] Voluntary labeling regulations in every country.

Table 4.23. Simulation Results: Canada, the US and the EU Produce Conventional Wheat, and Argentina and the Rest of the Developing Countries Produce GM Wheat ($Million: 2001)

Absolute Changes in $ million/yr	Canada	US	Argentina	Region B	Region C	Sum
Producer Surplus	-100	-260	111	177	1,835	1,763
Consumer Surplus	-38	-392	3	-601	1,543	516
Total Surplus	-138	-652	114	-423	3,379	2,280

Source: Calculated from Gruère and Carter (2004) model.

Conclusion

In this chapter, we presented the results of research on the farm-level benefits of adopting GM wheat. These results show that the net benefits of licensing GM wheat are quite large. We then use the farm-level results to calculate aggregate benefits and costs of introducing GM wheat in Canada. We compare the aggregate benefit-cost ratio to the threshold suggested by real options theory. We find that the benefit-cost ratio of introducing GM wheat is well above the conservative standard set by the real options analysis, indicating that the time to introduce GM wheat is here. This is true for a plausible range of the underlying agronomic assumptions. The decision to withhold GM wheat from the market in North America has already been made, but if Roundup Ready® or other types of GM wheat are adopted by competing exporters, big losers are prairie wheat farmers.

REFERENCES

Ahmed, F. A. "Detection of Genetically Modified Organisms in Foods." *Trends in Biotechnology* 20(2002):215-223.

Alston, J. M., J. Hyde, M. C. Marra, and P. D. Mitchell. "An Ex Ante Analysis of the Benefits from the Adoption of Corn Rootworm Resistant Transgenic Corn Technology." *AgBioForum* 5(2003):71-84.

Annou, M., E. Wailes, and G. Cramer. "Economic Analysis of Adopting Liberty Link Rice." in *Rice: Situation and Outlook Yearbook*. USDA-ERS, RCS-2000, Washington, D.C., November, 2000: 55-61.

Antle, J. M. and V. H. Smith (eds.) *The Economics of World Wheat Markets*. New York: CABI Publishing. 1999.

Australian Productivity Commission, *Single-desk Marketing: Assessing the Economic Arguments*. Productivity Staff Research paper, AusInfo, Canberra, 2000.

Benbrook, C. "The Farm-Level Economic Impacts of Bt Corn from 1996 through 2001: An Independent National Assessment." Benbrook Consulting, Idaho. 2001.

Bernauer, T. and E. Meins. "Scientific Revolution Meets Policy and the Market: Explaining Cross-National Differences in Agricultural Biotechnology Regulation." CIES Discussion Paper 0144, November, University of Adelaide. 2001.

Blackshaw, R.E. and K. N. Harker. "Selective Weed Control with Glyphosate in Glyphosate-Resistant Spring Wheat." *Weed Technology*. 16(2002):885–892.

Brimner, T.A., G. J. Gallivan, and G. R. Stephenson "Influence of herbicide-resistant canola on the environmental impact of weed management." *Pest Management Science*. 61 (2005):47-52.

Brookes, G. and P. Barfoot. "GM Rice: Will This Lead the Way for Global Acceptance of GM Crop Technology?" The International Service for the Acquisition of Agri-biotech Applications (ISAAA) Briefs no. 28, Ithaca, NY, 2003, available at www.isaaa.org.

Bullock, D.S. and M. Desquilbet. "The Economics of Non-GMO Segregation and Identity Preservation." *Food Policy* 27(2002): 81-99.

Canadian Biotechnology Advisory Committee "Improving the Regulation of Genetically Modified Foods and Other Novel Foods in Canada" Report to the Government of Canada, August 2002.

Canadian Grain Commission, "Improving Canada's Quality Assurance System: A Discussion Paper on the Use of Variety Eligibility Declarations." Winnipeg. January 14, 2003.

Canadian Grain Commission. "Update on the Varietal Eligibility Declaration (VED) Proposal." Winnipeg, December 2003.

Canadian Grain Commission. "Current CGC Position on Genetically Modified (GMO) Grains." Mimeo. Winnipeg, May 2000.

Canadian Grain Commission and others. "Identity Preserved Systems in the Canadian Grain System: A Discussion paper." Winnipeg, December 1998.

Canadian Grain Commission and others. *The Canadian Identity Preserved Recognition System.* Promotional Brochure. Winnipeg, 2002.

Canadian Grain Commission and Canadian Wheat Board. "Western Canada's Wheat Quality Control System: Future Directions." mimeo. Winnipeg, 1996.

Canada Grains Council. *Additional Transportation and Handling Costs for Identity Preservation of Bulk Grain Shipments in Canada.* Prepared by Canada Grains Council for APPAMEX. Winnipeg, August 2003.

Canada Grains Council. *Protein Premiums for Wheat in Canada.* Winnipeg. 1989.

Canola Council of Canada. *An Agronomic and Economic Assessment of Transgenic Canola.* January, 2001. Available at http://www.canola-council.org/production/gmo_toc.html

Carter, C. A. *An Economic Analysis of a Single North American Barley Market.* Report for Agriculture Canada, March, 1993.

Carter, C. A. and G. P. Gruère. "International Approach to GM Food Labeling," *Choices*, Second Quarter (2003):1–4. Available at: http://www.choicesmagazine.org/. a

Carter, C. A. and G. P. Gruère. "Mandatory labeling of genetically modified food: does it really provide consumer choice?" *AgBioForum*. 6(2003):1–5. Available at http://www.agbioforum.org. b

Carter, C. A. and R.M. A. Loyns. *The Economics of Single Desk Selling of Western Canadian Grain*. report prepared for Alberta Agriculture, Edmonton, March 1996.

Carter, C.A. and R.M.A. Loyns. *The Federal Government and the Prairie Grain Sector: A Study of Over-Regulation*. Toronto: University of Toronto Press. 1998.

Carter, C.A., R.M.A. Loyns and Z. F. Ahmadi-Esfahani. "Varietal Licensing Standards and Canadian Wheat Exports." *Canadian Journal of Agricultural Economics* 34 (1986): 361-77.

Carter, C.A, R.M.A. Loyns, and D. Berwald. "Domestic Costs of Statutory Marketing Authorities: The Case of the Canadian Wheat Board." *American Journal of Agricultural Economics*. 80 (1998): 313-24.

Carter, C. A., D. MacLaren, and A. Yilmaz, "How Competitive is the World Wheat Market?" Dept. of Agr. Econ., University of California, Davis, 1999, Working Paper 99-002. http://repositories.cdlib.org/are/arewp/99-002.

Carter, C. A., C. Revoredo and V. H. Smith. "The Longer-run Dynamics of World Wheat Prices: The Role of Stocks" in J.M. Antle and V.H. Smith (eds.) *The Economics of World Wheat Markets*. New York: CABI Publishing. 1999.

Dahl, B. L., and W. W. Wilson. "Grades/Classes of Hard Wheats Exported from North America: Analysis of Growth and Market Segments." *Review of Agricultural Economics* 22 (2000):172-91.

Dahl, B. L. and W. W. Wilson. *The Logistical Costs of Marketing Identity Preserved Wheat*. Agribusiness and Applied Economics Report No. 495. Agricultural Experiment Station, NDSU, Fargo N.D. August 2002.

Downie, R.K. and H. Beckie. "Isolation Effectiveness in Canola Pedigree Seed Production." Agriculture and Agri-Food Canada, Saskatoon Research Centre, 2002.

Ekboir, J. "Can Mercosur Feed the World? An Assessment of Mercosur's Agricultural Potential." Working Paper, CIMMYT, Mexico City, 2001.

Estey, W. Z. *Grain Handling and Transportation Review*. Report to the Canadian Minister of Transport. Ottawa. December 1998.

Fernandez-Cornejo, J. and W.D. McBride. "Genetically Engineered Crops for Pest Management in US Agriculture." USDA-ERS, Agricultural Economics Report 786, April 2000. Available at http://www.ers.usda.gov/publications/aer786/

Food and Agriculture Organization of the United Nations (FAO). The State of Food Insecurity in the World. Rome. 2004. available at: http://www.fao.org/documents/show_cdr.asp?url_file=/docrep/007/y5650e/y5650e00.htm

Foster, M. *Genetically modified grains, Market implications for Australian grain growers*. Technical Report, Australian Bureau of Agricultural and Resource Economics (ABARE) 2001.

Foster, M., P. Berry, and J. Hogan. *Market Access Issues for GM Products: Implications for Australia*. Australian Bureau of Agricultural and Resource Economics (ABARE) eReport 03.13 to the Department of Agriculture, Fisheries and Forestry, 2003.

F.O. Licht "World Commodity Markets: Monthly." No. 41., May 2004. www.agra-net.com.

Fulton, M. and L. Keyowski. "The Producer Benefits of Herbicide-Resistant Canola." *AgBioForum* 2(2), 1999, 85-93.

Furtan, W.H., R.S. Gray and J.J. Holzman. "Regulatory Approval Decisions in the Presence of Market Uncertainties: The Case of Genetically Modified Wheat." University of Saskatchewan Department of Agricultural Economics Working Paper. 2003. a.

Furtan, W.H., R.S. Gray, and J.J. Holzman. "The Optimal Time to License a Biotech Lemon." *Contemporary Economic Policy*. 21 (2003): 433-444. b.

Gene Technology Grains Committee. *Canola Industry Stewardship Principles, For Coexistence of Production Systems and Supply Chains.* Canberra, Australia. July 2003.

Gianessi, L. P., C. S. Silvers, S. Sankula, and J. E. Carpenter. "Plant Biotechnology: Current and Potential Impact for Improving Pest Management in US Agriculture: An Analysis of 40 Case Studies." National Center for Food and Agricultural Policy, Washington, D.C., 2002.

Glover J. "Gene flow study: Implications for the release of genetically modified crops in Australia" Department of Agriculture, Fisheries and Forestry, Australia, 2002.

Gosnell, D. "Non-GM Wheat Segregation Strategies: Comparing the Costs." M.Sc. thesis, University of Saskatchewan, Fall 2001.

Grain Cleaning Consortium. *The Economics of Cleaning Grain on the Prairies.* Prepared for Agriculture and Agri-Food Canada. Winnipeg, 1998.

Grain Industry Working Group on Genetically Modified Wheat. *Conditions for the Introduction of Genetically Modified Wheat.* February 5, 2003. Available at http://www.cwb.ca/en/topics/biotechnology/pdf/gmowheat.pdf

Gray, R. "The Economics of Herbicide-Tolerant Wheat and Bifurcation of World Markets." Ch.9 in *The Future of Food: Biotechnology Markets and Policies in an International Setting.* P.G. Pardey (ed). John Hopkins University Press. 2001.

Gruère, G. and C. A. Carter. "Should genetically modified food labeling policies be harmonized?" working paper. Dept. of Agricultural and Resource Economics. University of California, Davis. 2004. Available at http://ccarter.ucdavis.edu/carterpaper.htm

Haddow, P. "Health, Plant and Animal Protection, and Food Safety: WTO and NAFTA." In R.M.A. Loyns et al. (eds). *Keeping the Borders Open.* Proceedings of the Eighth Policy Disputes Information Workshop. University of Guelph, Texas A&M University and El Colegio de México. Friesens Printers: Winnipeg, 2004.

Henning, J.C., and L. Martin. "An Economic Evaluation of Expanded Canadian 3-M Wheat Exports." *Canadian Journal of Agricultural Economics* 37(1989):445-65.

Holzman, J. "The Economics of Herbicide Tolerant Wheat in Western Canadian Crop Rotations." M.Sc. thesis, University of Saskatchewan. 2001.

Hjort, K. C. "Class and Source Substitutability in the Demand for Imported Wheat." Ph.D. dissertation, Purdue University, 1988.

Huang J., Rozelle S., Pray C. and Q. Wang. 2002. "Plant Biotechnology in China." *Science*. v295(2002):674-676.

Huygen, I., M. Veeman, and M. Lerohl "Cost Implications of Alternative GM Tolerance Levels: Non-Genetically Modified Wheat in Western Canada." *Agbioforum*, 6(4) 2003: http://www.agbioforum.org/v6n4/index.htm.

International Grains Council, "Grain Market Report." Various issues, International Grains Council, London, England.

International Service for the Acquisition of Agri-biotech Applications (ISAAA). "2002 Global GM Crop Area Continues to Grow for the Sixth Consecutive Year at a Sustained Rate of More than 10%." 2003 Available at www.isaaa.org.

Irvine, G.N. "Technological Advances in the Milling and Baking Industries and their Effects Upon Markets For Canadian Wheat." In Loyns, R.M.A. (ed). *Seminar on Wheat*. University of Manitoba, Department of Agricultural Economics, Winnipeg 1970.

Kalaitzandonakes, N. and J. Bijman. "Who is driving biotechnology acceptance?" *Nature Biotechnology*. 21 (2003):366-369.

Kidnie, M.J., R. C. Ripley, J. J. McNulty, and R. A. Neyedley. "Performance of Roundup Transorb Compared To Commercial Standard Herbicides In Roundup Ready Wheat." Canadian Weed Science Society, Dec. 2003.

Klein, K.K., C.A. Webber, and J.D. Graham. "Medium Quality Wheat Production on the Canadian Prairies: An Economic Assessment." Marketing and Economics Branch, Agric. Canada, Ottawa, 1986. 173 pages.

Koo, W. W., W. Mao, and T. Sakurai. "Wheat Demand in Japanese Flour Milling Industry: A Production Theory Approach." *Agricultural Economics* 24 (2001):167-78.

Kosior, Jake. "A Mixed Logistics Strategy for Canadian Grain: Discussion Paper." *23rd Australian Research Forum.* Perth, Australia. September 29-October 1, 1999.

Kosior, J., B. E. Prentice and E. Vido. "A Mixed Logistics Strategy for Grain: The Competitiveness of Containers Versus Bulk." The Transport Institute, University of Manitoba, Winnipeg. October 2002.

Koziel, M. G.; Beland, G. L.; Bowman, C.; Carozzi, N. B.; Crenshaw, R.; Crossland, L.; Dawson, J.; Desai, N.; Hill, M.; Kadwell, S.; Launis, K.; Lewis, K.; Maddox, D.; McPherson, K.; Meghji, M. R.; Merlin, E.; Rhodes, R.; Warren, G. W.; Wright, M.; Evola, S. V. "Field performance of elite transgenic maize plants expressing an insecticidal protein derived from Bacillus thuringiensis." *Biotechnology* 11(1993):194-200.

KPMG Management Consulting. *Rapid Grain Flow-Transforming Grain Logistics.* Calgary, Alberta, April 1995.

Kraft, D.F., W.H. Furtan, and E. W. Tyrchniewicz. *Performance Evaluation of the Canadian Wheat Board.* Winnipeg: Canadian Wheat Board, January 1996.

Kuntz, G.M. "Transgenic Wheat: Potential Price Impacts for Canada's Wheat Export Market" M.Sc. thesis, University of Saskatchewan, Fall 2001.

Lin, W. "Estimating the costs of segregation for non-biotech maize and soybeans." In V. Santaniello, R.E. Evenson, and D. Zilberman (eds.), *Market Development for Genetically Modified Foods.* Wallingford, UK: CABI Publishing. 2002.

Lin, W., G.K. Price, and E. Allen, "StarLink: Impacts on the US Corn Market and World Trade" USDA, Economic Research Service, paper presented at American Agricultural Economics Association Annual Meeting, Long Beach, California, July, 2002.

Longmire, J. and A. Moldashev "Wheat in Kazakhstan–Changing Competitiveness and Sources of Productivity Growth." *CIMMYT 1998-99 World Wheat Facts and Trends. Global Wheat Research in a Changing World: Challenges and Achievements.* P.L. Pingali, ed., Mexico D.F.:CIMMYT, 1999.

Loyns, R.M.A. and C. A. Carter. *Grains in Western Canadian Economic Development to 1990.* Economic Council of Canada Discussion Paper No. 272. September 1984.

Manitoba Agriculture, Food, and Rural Initiatives, *Guide to Crop Protection 2003*, Winnipeg, 2003. Available at: http://www.gov.mb.ca/agriculture/crops/cropproduction/gaa01d01.html

Manitoba Rural Adaptation Council Inc. and Canadian Wheat Board. "The Market Competitiveness of Western Canadian Wheat." Winnipeg, January 1999.

Marra, M.C., Pardey, P.G., and Alston. J.M. "The Payoffs to Transgenic Field Crops: An Assessment of the Evidence." *AgBioForum*, 5(2002):1-8. Available at http://www.agbioforum.org

Martin, L., H. Mayer and J. Bouma. *Benefits and Costs of a Voluntary Wheat Board.* Report prepared for the Province of Alberta. George Morris Center. Calgary, March, 2002.

McBride, W.D. and N. Brooks. "Survey Evidence on Producer Use and Costs of Genetically Modified Seed." *Agribusiness.* 16 (2000):6-20.

McDonald, R.L. and D.R. Siegel. "The Value of Waiting to Invest." *Quarterly Journal of Economics* 101(1986):707-727.

Mitchener, B. 'Europe has no appetite for modified food.' *Wall Street Journal.* September 23, 2002, Section B, page 3, Column 1.

Monopolies and Mergers Commission. *A Report on the Merger Situation: Tompkins plc and Kerry Group plc.* UK Parliament, Cm 4031, 1998.

Nelson, G. C., *Genetically Modified Organisms in Agriculture*, Economics and Politics, Academic Press, 2001.

Nelson, R., Barrett, D., Foster M., Turner S., and Beasley, A. *The future of canola production in Australia*. ABARE Research report 01.6, Canberra. 2001

Noussair, C., S. Robin and B. Ruffieux "Do Consumers Really Refuse to Buy Genetically Modified Food?" *The Economic Journal* 114 (2004): 102–120.

Paarlberg, R. L. "The Contested Governance of GM Foods: Implications for US-EU Trade and the Developing World," Weatherhead Center for International Affairs at Harvard University August 2002.

Paarlberg, Robert L. "The global food fight." *Foreign Affairs* 79(2000):24-38.

Parsons, G. and W. W. Wilson. "Grain Handling and Transportation Systems: A Canada – United States Comparison." Organization for Western Economic Cooperation, Regina, 1999.

Phillips, P.W.B. and D. Corkindale. "Marketing GM Foods: The Way Forward." *AgBioForum* 5(2002):113-121. Available at www.agbioforum.org.

Phillips, P.W.B. and H. McNeill, "A Survey of National Labeling Policies for GM foods." *AgBioForum*. 3(2000):219–224. Available at http://www.agbioforum.org.

Prairie Horizons Ltd. and JRG Consulting Group. The Economics of Cleaning Grain on the Prairies. Prepared for Agriculture and Agri-Food Canada, Ottawa. September, 1998. available at: http://www.agr.gc.ca/mad-dam/e/winne/clean1e_s.pdf

Rauch, J. "Will Frankenfood Save the Planet?" *The Atlantic Monthly*. October 2003.

Reichert, H. and K. Vachal. *Identity Preserved Grain-A Logistical Overview*. USDA and Upper Great Plains Transportation Institute. January 2000.

Remple. C. and J. McNulty "Roundup Ready System for Wheat Production." Canadian Weed Science Society, Proceedings of the 2002 National Meeting, Saskatoon, Nov. 2002: 125-139.

Saskatchewan Agriculture, Food, and Rural Revitalization, *Crop Planning Guide 2004*, Regina, 2004. Available for various crops and soil zones at: http://www.agr.gov.sk.ca/DOCS/Econ_Farm_Man/Production/Cereals /cropplanguide.asp

Schnepf, R. and E. Dohlman "Argentina and Brazil Sharpen Their Competitive Edge." *Agricultural Outlook*, Economic Research Service, USDA, September 2001.

Serecon Management Consulting Inc. and Koch Paul Associates "An Agronomic And Economic Assessment Of Transgenic Canola." report prepared for the Canola Council of Canada, January 2001.

Sheldon, I., "Regulation of Biotechnology: Will we ever 'Freely' Trade GMOs?" *European Review of Agricultural Economics*. 29(2002):155–176.

Smyth, S. and Phillips, P.W.B. "Competitors Co-operating: Establishing a Supply Chain to Manage Genetically Modified Canola." *International Food and Agribusiness Management Review*. 3(2001): 51-66.

Smyth, S. and Phillips, P.W.B. "Product differentiation alternatives: identity preservation, segregation, and traceability." *AgBioForum*, 5(2003): 30-42.

Sparks Companies Inc. *Downstream Wheat Industry Analysis*. March 2001.

Stone, S., A. Matysek, and A. Dolling. *Modelling Possible Impacts of GM Crops on Australian Trade*. Productivity Commission Staff Research Paper, Melbourne, October 2002,

Taylor, R. D., E. A. DeVuyst, and W. K.Woo. "Potential Impacts of GM Wheat on United States and Northern Plains Wheat Trade." Agribusiness & Applied Economics Report No. 515, Center for Agricultural Policy and Trade Studies, Department of Agribusiness and Applied Economics, North Dakota State University, Fargo, ND. May 2003.

Uchtmann, D.L. "StarLink–A Case Study of Agricultural Biotechnology Regulation." *Drake Journal of Agricultural Law* 7(2002):159-211.

Ulrich, A., Furtan, W. H., and A. Schmitz. "The Cost of a Licensing System Regulation: An Example from Canadian Prairie Agriculture." *Journal of Political Economy* 95(February 1987):160-78.

UK GM Science Review Panel. "GM Science Review." Report prepared for UK Secretary of State for the Environment, Food and Rural Affairs. 2004. Available at: http://www.gmsciencedebate.org.uk.

US Department of Agriculture. *Embargoes, Surplus Disposal, and US Agriculture.* Washington DC: Economic Research Service, Ag. Econ. Report No. 564, 1986.

US Department of Agriculture. *Wheat: Situation and Outlook Yearbook.* Washington DC: Economic Research Service, various years.

US Department of Agriculture. *Indonesia: Grain and Feed Wheat Update 2002.* Foreign Agricultural Service GAIN Report #ID2017, September 17, 2002.

US Department of Agriculture. *Japan Biotechnology Update on Japan's Biotechnology Safety Approval and Labeling Policies.* Foreign Agricultural Service, GAIN Report #JA3002, February 28, 2003.

US Department of Agriculture. *Shrinking Middle East Wheat Imports have Global Implications.* Foreign Agricultural Service, International Trade Report, January 14, 2004.

US Department of Agriculture. *US Trade Exports - FATUS Commodity Aggregations Database,* Foreign Agricultural Service, various years, available via the World Wide Web at http://www.fas.usda.gov/ustrade.

Vocke, G. *Wheat: Background and Issues for Farm Legislation.* Washington DC: Economic Research Service, USDA, WHS-0701-01, July 2001.

Wainio, J. and T. Raney. *Argentina's Economic Reforms Expand Growth Potential for Agriculture.* Agricultural Outlook, Economic Research Service, USDA, March 1998.

Western Grain Marketing Panel "Report of the Western Grain Marketing Panel." Winnipeg: July 1996.

Western Grains Research Foundation. *Industry Report.* "National Workshop Tackles Fusarium". Saskatoon, February 2004.

Wilhelm, C. J. "Non-Transgenic Grain Segregation at Country Elevators in South Dakota." M.Sc. thesis, South Dakota State University. 2003.

Wilson, W. W. "Differentiation and Implicit Prices in Export Wheat Markets." *Western Journal of Agricultural Economics* 14 (1989):67-77.

Wilson, W. W. "Demand for Wheat Classes by Pacific Rim Countries." *Journal of Agricultural and Resource Economics* 19 (1994):197-209.

Wilson W. W. and B. L. Dahl "Costs and Risks of Testing and Segregating GM Wheat" Agribusiness and Applied Economics Report No. 501, North Dakota State University, 2002.

Wilson, W. W., and P. Gallagher. "Quality Differences and Price Responsiveness of Wheat Class Demands." *Western Journal of Agricultural Economics* 15 (1990):254-64.

Wilson, W. W., E. J. Jabs and B. L. Dahl. *Optimal Testing Strategies for Genetically Modified Wheat.* Department of Agribusiness and Applied Economics, Agricultural Experiment Station. North Dakota State University. Fargo. August 2003.

Wilson, W. W., E. L. Janzen, and B. L. Dahl. "Issues in Development and Adoption of Genetically Modified (GM) Wheats." *AgBioForum* 6(3), 2003.

Wilson, W. W., E. L. Janzen, B. L. Dahl and C. Wachenheim. *Issues in Development and Adoption of Genetically Modified (GM) Wheats.* Agribusiness and Applied Economics Report No. 509. Agricultural Experiment Station, NDSU, Fargo N.D. January 2003.

Wilson, W. W., and T. Preszler. "End-Use Performance Uncertainty and Competition in International Wheat Markets." *American Journal of Agricultural Economics* 74 (1992):556-63.

Wilson, W. W. and T. Preszler. "Quality and Price Competition in International Wheat Trade: A Case Study of the United Kingdom Wheat Import Market." *Agribusiness* 9 (1993):377-389

Wisner, Robert. *Market Risks of Genetically Modified Wheat.* Working paper, Dept. of Economics, Iowa State University, October 2003.

World Health Organization. "Safety Aspects of Genetically Modified Foods of Plant Origin" Report of a Joint FAO/WHO Expert Consultation on Foods Derived from Biotechnology, WHO, Geneva, 2002.

END NOTES

1   The terms GM wheat, biotech wheat, Roundup Ready® wheat, and herbicide tolerant (HT) wheat are used interchangeably in this book.
2   These statistics on transgenic crops were obtained from the International Service for the Acquisition of Agri-biotech Applications–ISAAA–www.isaaa.org.
3   For a discussion of the issues associated with the commercialization of GM wheat, with a US focus, see Wilson, Janzen, and Dahl.
4   One example is a speech given by Adrian Measner, CWB President and CEO, to the National Grain Trade Council in 2003. His speech was entitled "Challenges to the Canadian Grain Industry" and is available at: http://www.cwb.ca/en/news/speeches/2003/091803.jsp. In this speech, Mr. Measner outlined why the CWB is against Roundup Ready® wheat. He argued that more than 82% of foreign customers would no longer buy Canadian wheat and this would devastate the Canadian grain industry.
5   The working group's report is available at http://www.cwb.ca/en/topics/biotechnology/pdf/gmowheat.pdf.
6   See Chapter 3 for a discussion of the differences between an *identity preservation* (IP) and a *segregation* system. Normally, an IP program identifies the source and variety of the grain and maintains that identity throughout the marketing chain. Alternatively, a *segregation* system keeps a given variety or type of grain apart from others and uses bulk handling. The Canadian system segregates into grade categories that groups like-varieties and separates them from unlike-varieties.
7   See the editorial by Gord Flaten, entitled "Biotech wheat needs a cost-benefit analysis" in *Food Traceability Report*, February 2003, Vol. 3, No. 2. Flaten is director of market development for the CWB.
8   See testimony of Mr. Ken Ritter, Chair, Board of Directors, Canadian Wheat Board, Standing Committee on Agriculture and Agri-Food, 37th Parliament, 2nd Session, April 3, 2003.
9   See testimony by Mr. Ken Ritter, Chair, Board of Directors, CWB, to Standing Committee on Agriculture and Agri-Food, 37th Parliament, 1st Session, Nov. 1, 2001; and testimony to Standing Committee 37th Parliament, 2nd Session, April 3, 2003.

10 For example, see www.afro.who.int/press/2002/pr20020828.html.
11 www.agentur-baums.de/food-monitor/dokumente/docs/ebs_177_en.pdf, p. 1.
12 www.foodstandards.gov.uk/news/pressreleases/cas2003press.
13 www.abeurope.info/images/files/abe_issues_paper_7.pdf.
14 The earlier 1996 Carter and Loyns study is available at http://www.agric.gov.ab.ca/economic/market/sngldesk.html.
15 Many importers of wheat report that mills routinely clean the product before it goes into their mills (one miller claimed the wheat may be cleaned twice) even if it comes from Canada. That means that some Canadian wheat is cleaned three times before it goes through a mill. Screenings are an important source of animal feed in many countries and it is not unusual to have feed mills as part of flour milling operations.
16 Adrian Measner "Golden Opportunities: The Future of the Canadian Wheat and Barley Trade" presentation to Agricore United Annual Members' Meeting, Edmonton, Feb. 12, 2004.
17 One might observe that supply management represents more extensive regulation but it is designed for domestic, not export, conditions.
18 GM cotton is grown in Australia and cotton oil is a food byproduct.
19 They did not consider wheat in their economic model.
20 Warburton is a UK bakery. See Chapter 3 for a full discussion of the Warburton procurement program.
21 The Canadian Grain Commission's Variety Eligibility Declaration (VED) proposal was withdrawn in December 2003. Chapter 3 discusses this issue in detail. VED would have introduced a modern system of grain segregation supported by declarations every time grain changes hands, and backed by laboratory testing. We believe that VED may have been opposed by the CWB and the wheat processors because VED would have facilitated a smoother and less costly introduction of GM wheat in Canada.
22 The Cartagena Protocol on Biosafety illustrates the huge gap between Canada/US and the EU, when it comes to the acceptance of GM crops. The Cartagena Protocol aims to regulate trade in GM foods and it embodies the "precautionary principle" which views GM crops as possibly risky unless proved to be safe. Canada has signed the protocol but has not ratified it, while the US remains a non-Party to the Protocol. For more information go to http://www.biodiv.org/default.aspx.
23 www.ncfap.org.

24　The latest EU regulations on the traceability and labeling of GM foods and of Food and Feed Products produced from GM crops ((EC) No 1830/2003) and on GM food and feed ((EC) No 1829/2003) were implemented in June 2004. For a description of the EU labeling regulations, go to http://europa.eu.int/comm/food/food/biotechnology/gmfood/index_en.htm.

25　The voluntary labeling standards are available at the Canadian General Standards Board website www.cgsb.gc.ca.

26　We have excluded the 2002/03 crop year, marked by a serious crop failure in Canada due to drought.

27　Estimated with regression analysis, the annual average growth in wheat yields is not statistically different from zero, excluding the 2002/03 crop when yields plummeted due to the drought.

28　From 1996 to 2003, US spring wheat acreage fell from 20 to 13.8 million acres, and winter wheat declined from 51 to 44 million acres.

29　International Grains Council, GMR No. 329, Nov. 27, 2003

30　USDA, FAS, Jan. 2004.

31　See the Population Reference Bureau www.prb.org.

32　See Carter, Loyns, and Ahmadi-Esfahani, 1986; and Henning and Martin, 1989.

33　International Grains Council, GMR Report No. 329, Nov. 27th, 2003

34　USDA, Foreign Agricultural Service, GAIN Report #KZ3007, August 2003.

35　See the FAO's *Food Outlook*, February 2001 and the USDA's WASDE, May 10, 2001.

36　UK Monopolies and Mergers Commission, A Report on the Merger Situation, presented to Parliament by the Secretary of State for Trade and Industry, 1988.

37　National Association of British and Irish Millers (www.nabim.org.uk).

38　Chapter 3 discusses the Warburton program in greater detail.

39　See Canadian Grain Commission, Update on the Variety Eligibility Declaration (VED) Proposal, December 2003.

40　JA Zenchu's website (in English) is: http://www.e-zenchu-ja.org/.

41　See the MAFF website: http://www.maff.go.jp/eindex.html.

42　USDA, FAS, GAIN Report #ID2017.

43　Indonesian Flour Mills Association, January 2001.

44　FAS, USDA, China Grain and Feed Annual 2004, GAIN Report #CH4005, February 20, 2004.

45 USDA FAS, China Grain and Feed Annual, GAIN Report CH4005, Feb. 2004.

46 USDA, FAS, KFDA Biotech Labeling Standards for Processed Foods, GAIN Report #KS1046, August 23, 2001.

47 USDA, FAS, Korea, Republic of Oilseeds and Products Annual 2002, GAIN Report #KS2008, February 27, 2002.

48 The formula for the import demand elasticity is $\epsilon_I = (1/s)\,\epsilon_D - [(1-s)/s]\eta_S$, where s is market share, ϵ_D is domestic demand elasticity, and η_S is the domestic supply elasticity.

49 For further discussion of grain cleaning in Canada see Prairie Horizons Ltd. and JRG Consulting Group.

50 For instance see April 3, 2003 CWB News Release, "CWB urges federal government of close gap on GM wheat," and May 27, 2003 CWB News Release, "CWB asks Monsanto to put the brakes on Roundup Ready® wheat." These news releases are available at http://www.cwb.ca/en/news/releases/2003/index.jsp.

51 See the CWB "Closing the Regulatory Gap: Industry Supported Solutions for Genetically Modified Wheat" presentation to the House of Commons Standing Committee on Agriculture and Agri-Food, April 3, 2003.

52 Eric Schroeder "Identity Preservation: Capturing Quality and Delivering Consistency." *Milling and Baking News.* June 19, 2001:24-28.

53 CGC and CWB *Western Canada's Wheat Quality Control System: Future Directions.* pp 3-4. The Western Grains Research Foundation identifies KVD as one of the critical constraints on new variety development in wheat in relation to fusarium headblight.

54 The definitions of "IP" and "foreign material" used here are slightly more general than those used by the CGC. The differences do not affect the discussion.

55 American Seed Trade Association, *Standardization of Seed Testing Protocols for Adventitious Presence.* Undated, (www.amseed.com).

56 The literature on grain marketing, segregation and grading certainly recognizes this point in a general way. Wilson, Jabs and Dahl make the point explicitly.

57 This position is consistent with the Canadian Grain Industry Working Group on Genetically Modified Wheat. It is also the way that canola was segregated in the first two years of GM canola production on the prairies in 1995 and 1996.

58 See Glover for evidence that this condition is easily met for wheat.

59 Canadian Grain Commission, January 14, 2003.

60 The CGC does not consider VED as an IP system because it is applied to the entire bulk handling system and it does not necessarily generate price premiums.

61 Canadian Grain Commission, *Update on the Variety Eligibility Declaration (VED) Proposal.* December 2003.

62 Canadian Grain Commission, Canadian Seed Institute, Canadian Soybean Export Association, *The Canadian Identity Preserved Recognition System.* Undated.

63 See the Canadian Seed Growers Association website, *www.seedgrowers.ca.*

64 These conclusions were developed in personal communication with seed dealers, and confirmed from historic information from SeCan. The spread between the CWB final wheat price and certified seed costs has been recorded since 1986. The range was $82/mt (1998) to $7/mt (1992) with an unweighted mean of $45/mt ($1.23/bu). The time frame is long enough to average out market noise between CWB final prices and seed prices paid at least eighteen months earlier. In relative terms the seed prices ranged from 144 to 105 percent above CWB prices, which agrees with the observations above. Source: Larry White, SeCan Ottawa.

65 Based on interviews with personnel at Canamera Foods in Altona and Toronto.

66 "Grainfetti" is a simple but effective tool commercialized on the prairies during a period of high grain prices in the 1970s when on-farm theft was a problem. It is basically numbered (and registered) confetti which is placed in the grain for storage. It can only be removed by cleaning the grain. The concept, applied in the form of a compatible edible foodstuff would appear to have many applications where more costly IP methods are being used. The egg industry in Canada uses a variation on this technology to differentiate between table and breaker eggs. The lower priced breaker eggs are marked with vegetable dye.

67 For the 2004 crop, Cargill is reported to have contracted 750,000 acres of a proprietary canola, developed for its high-oleic, low-linoleic trans-fat characteristics. The canola will be identity preserved and carries a premium of about $50/mt. (AGRIWEEK, Feb. 9.04). At a relatively low 30 bu./ac. average, that acreage represents at least half a million tonnes which would make it a much larger program than HAR.

68 This conclusion contradicts the evidence provided in the August 2003 report by the CGC. That analysis used segregation in malting barley as the norm against which to estimate IP costs and it produced large IP costs.

69 Based on discussions with officials with Agricore United, the CWB website, previous interviews with Anheuser Busch in St. Louis, and other elevator companies.

70 The "equal to" criterion for registering new varieties of wheat on the prairies has a long history, beginning with the variety Marquis decades ago. The concept was that when new varieties were presented by plant breeders for registration, that they should be at least as good as the standard that was being grown at the time. Marquis wheat gave way to Thatcher, which gave way to Neepawa. More recently the concept of using mean characteristics of check varieties has replaced Neepawa as the standard. The primary considerations relate to quality characteristics of the new variety, but agronomic and disease characteristics are indirectly reflected in the process of eliminating and accepting new varieties, in the words of one plant breeder "to assure the bar is always being raised." At the time that Warburton was selecting varieties and regions for sourcing their wheat from Canada, the "equal-to-Neepawa" standard was still in place.

71 This comment was made by a member of the UK milling and baking industry, but variations on the same message were common in UK and Canadian interviews.

72 Personal communication, May and November, 2003.

73 Among other over-estimates of costs in that report are is the excessive testing estimates that did not reflect new, low-cost test procedures. There is no total of testing costs provided but the estimates were based on CGC information for DNA testing at $10 per kernel, representing several dollars per tonne in total. Those numbers are, at best, seriously outdated. This source also had elevators closed down for 3 days to clean a leg, and one to two weeks to clean the entire system. There was no consideration given to ISO certified operations.

74 This analysis specifically analyzed a common facility for receiving producer wheat, treating GM wheat as "just another commodity." (Gosnell, p.101).

75 Gosnell did not build contamination into his simulation model. Instead he did a separate risk analysis on the final results by assuming that some contaminated vessels would be sold at a low salvage value.

76 Gosnell (p.43) tabulated two US soybean and two corn IP estimates which ranged from 29 US cents to 54 cents US per bushel, and the Canadian canola estimates discussed earlier of $C 33/mt to $C43/mt. These are all different estimates than Wilson et al. reported.

77 It is common practice for HTP elevators to offer "trucking premiums' to induce delivery for a particular grain sale, and to capture rail car rate discounts. The amount of the premium may be $3/mt to $5/mt. but amounts over $10/mt are sometimes paid.

78 The issue of contracting the non-GM production is not addressed directly but it is recognized that contracting would facilitate most of the arguments made in this section.

79 It is noted that if call-ups were scheduled, by chance or by design, to assure non-GM was delivered before any GM wheat went through the elevator, the clean up costs for that call would disappear. Except for feed wheat and random deliveries of ends of bins or seed plant screenings, the CWB would have the ability to achieve this result on some occasions, and in some areas.

80 http://www1.agric.gov.ab.ca/app19/calc/index.jsp?type=Crop

81 Genetically modified wheat will allow additional flexibility in crop rotations, the timing of herbicide applications, etc.

82 Clearfield® is herbicide-tolerant but is not classified as genetically modified, because it was not created using recombinant DNA techniques.

83 Holzman models the difference in price between GM and conventional wheat as a price discount for GM, rather than as a price premium for non-GM wheat. We believe producers of GM wheat will receive the baseline world price for wheat, and that non-GM producers will receive a premium from buyers willing to pay extra for conventional wheat.

84 On page 62 of his thesis, Holzman identifies the cost as $6.19 per acre, but the figures in his tables indicate that he used $4.13 per acre.

85 Low-disturbance tillage techniques have fewer tillage operations per crop, and increased herbicide applications for weed control, relative to conventional tillage techniques.

86 The use of a triangular distribution is based on Furtan, Gray and Holzman (2003b). The triangular distribution uses a "most-likely" value as it's center, and also sets a maximum and a minimum value for the estimated parameter.

87 Holzman reports this figure as $2.49 per acre, but our calculations suggest the figure should be $5.13 per acre.

88 Again we believe the figures reported by Holzman are inconsistent with his assumptions. In his study, he reported these figures as -$.47 per acre and $5.83 per acre, respectively.

89 This figure is 1.5 to 2 times the estimate we use in Chapter 3, to keep our calculations conservative.

90 We believe that their estimate of 2.27 was incorrectly calculated, and that the threshold, using their assumptions, should be lower. We use their published threshold here so our results can be easily compared to theirs.

91   Australia was excluded from Region A exporters because it has mandatory GM food labeling and it may be slow to adopt GM wheat.

92   The 10% yield increase for GM wheat used by Gruère and Carter is slightly higher than the 9% we assume for the rest of this chapter.